Walch Hands-on Science Series

Simple Machines

by Steven Souza and Joseph Shortell

illustrated by Lloyd Birmingham

Project editors: Carl Raab and Joel Beller

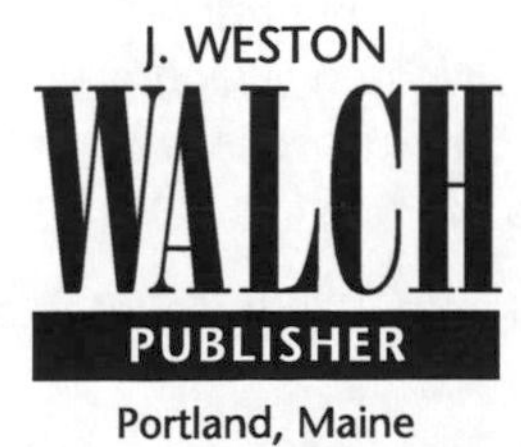

Portland, Maine

User's Guide
to
Walch Reproducible Books

As part of our general effort to provide educational materials that are as practical and economical as possible, we have designated this publication a "reproducible book." The designation means that purchase of the book includes purchase of the right to limited reproduction of all pages on which this symbol appears:

Here is the basic Walch policy: We grant to individual purchasers of this book the right to make sufficient copies of reproducible pages for use by all students of a single teacher. This permission is limited to a single teacher and does not apply to entire schools or school systems, so institutions purchasing the book should pass the permission on to a single teacher. Copying of the book or its parts for resale is prohibited.

Any questions regarding this policy or requests to purchase further reproduction rights should be addressed to:

Permissions Editor
J. Weston Walch, Publisher
321 Valley Street • P. O. Box 658
Portland, Maine 04104-0658

1 2 3 4 5 6 7 8 9 10

ISBN 0-8251-4263-6

J. Weston Walch, Publisher
P. O. Box 658 • Portland, Maine 04104-0658
www.walch.com

Printed in the United States of America

Contents

To the Teacher

This is one in a series of hands-on science activities for middle school and early high school students. A recent survey of middle school students conducted by the National Science Foundation (NSF) found that

- more than half listed science as their favorite subject.
- more than half wanted more hands-on activities.
- 90 percent stated that the best way for them to learn science was to do experiments themselves.

The books in this series seek to capitalize on these findings. These books are not texts but supplements. They offer hands-on, fun activities that will turn some students on to science. Most of these activities can be done in school, and some of them can be done at home. Most of the authors are teachers who have field-tested the activities in a public middle school and/or high school.

In this book, lessons explore the operations and applications of simple machines. Students will examine the concepts of force, work, power, efficiency, and mechanical advantage. They will also discover how simple machines like ramps, wedges, levers, pulleys, and gears operate. Students will begin to appreciate the diverse applications of simple machines, especially in everyday life. Activities range from the simple (What Is Work?) to the advanced (How Do Pulleys Work Together to Make a Better Machine?). There is something for every student. We strongly recommend that you try these activities yourself before asking your students to perform them.

Due to the rapid and constant evolution of the Internet, some sites may no longer be accessible at the addresses listed at the time of this printing.

THE ACTIVITIES CAN BE USED

- to provide hands-on experiences pertaining to textbook content.
- to give verbally limited children a chance to succeed and gain extra credit.
- as the basis for class or school science fair projects or for other science competitions.
- to involve students in science club activities.
- as homework assignments.
- to involve parents in their children's science education and experiences.
- to foster an appreciation for science.

This book provides hands-on activities in which students

- manipulate equipment.
- interpret data.
- evaluate experimental designs.
- draw inferences and conclusions.
- make predictions.
- apply the methods of science.

Each activity has a teacher resource section that includes, besides helpful hints and suggestions, a scoring rubric, a quiz, and Internet connections for those students who wish to carry out the Follow-up Activities. Instructional objectives and the National Science Standards that apply to each activity are provided in order for you to meet state and local expectations.

What Is a Force?

TEACHER RESOURCE PAGE

INSTRUCTIONAL OBJECTIVES

Students will be able to

- describe the physical concept of force.
- state Newton's first law of motion.
- predict how far a spring will stretch under a given force.

NATIONAL SCIENCE STANDARDS ADDRESSED

Students produce evidence that demonstrates understanding of

- motions and forces.

Students demonstrate scientific inquiry and problem-solving skills by

- identifying and controlling experimental variables.
- working individually and in teams to collect and share information and ideas.
- using technology and tools to observe and measure objects.

Students demonstrate effective scientific communication by

- arguing from evidence and data.

MATERIALS

For each student or group:

PART I

- Laboratory stand with an attachable clamp
- Two coil springs of differing stiffness
- Assorted lab weights, 1 to 10 newtons
- Spring scale (reading up to 20 newtons)
- Meter stick
- Vinyl electrical tape

PART II

- Table tennis or other smooth ball
- Smooth, level floor or table

HELPFUL HINTS AND DISCUSSION

Time frame: 40 minutes, or a single period of instruction

Structure: Individuals or cooperative learning groups

Location: In class

In this activity, students will be investigating the concept of **force**. They will see how a spring supplies more force the more it is stretched. Explain that **gravity** is also a force, which can be balanced by the upward force of the spring. Provide students with an assortment of springs of different constants, making sure before class to choose springs that stretch measurably with the available weights, but do not reach the table. Be sure to check that the weights do not stretch the springs permanently. You may use individual lab weights with hooks or loops, or a slotted weight set with a weight hanger.

Encourage students to be creative in Part II, step 2, but *in no case should the ball move until step 3.* If a student complains, "How can I move the ball if you won't let me do anything to it?" then the student is properly grasping the idea of Newton's first law of motion.

ADAPTATIONS FOR HIGH AND LOW ACHIEVERS

High Achievers: These students should be encouraged to do the Follow-up Activity. You can also guide them to a more mathematical treatment of the subject.

Low Achievers: These students can be paired with high achievers. Have lower achievers read and record the measurements from the meter stick to give them more experience with scientific tools.

SCORING RUBRIC

Full credit should be given to students whose data recorded in the Data Collection and Analysis section look reasonable, who correctly calculate distances the springs have stretched, and who answer the questions correctly and in complete sentences. Extra credit should be awarded to students who do the Extension and the Follow-up Activity. The quiz can be scored from 1 to 3 correct.

INTERNET TIE-INS

- For more on simple machines:
  http://sun.kent.wednet.edu/KSD/KR/ScienceDept/subjects/physicspages/Web/Wade/physics.htm
- For more on Newton's laws of motion:
  http://www.execpc.com/~culp/space/newton.html
  http://csep10.phys.utk.edu/astr161/lect/history/newton3laws.html

QUIZ

1. What is a force? What type of force (pull or push) does a spring provide when an object is suspended from that spring?
2. If a certain spring supplies 20 newtons of force when it is stretched 10 cm, how much force will it supply when a weight stretches the spring 5 cm?
3. What is required for a stationary object to begin moving?

Name ______________________________ Date ______________________

What is a Force?

STUDENT ACTIVITY PAGE

BEFORE YOU BEGIN

Three words you will often see on these pages are *force, work,* and *power.* You may think of "force" as something someone makes you do—like taking out the trash. However, in physics, **force** has a very specific meaning: **A force is either a push or a pull that causes an object to change its speed and/or direction of motion.**

In a science-fiction movie, you might see a spaceship fly through space. Its rocket engines are blazing. Then it comes to a halt when the rockets shut off. This, however, is not how the universe works. The Italian scientist Galileo Galilei found that if no forces act on an object, it will move in a straight line at constant speed. This would be the case of an unpowered spaceship far from any stars or planets. This property of matter is called **inertia**. The spaceship will only change direction or speed if a force is exerted on it. Isaac Newton called this the **first law of motion.**

In this activity, you will balance the weight of an object (a downward force) with the upward force that a spring supplies. You will see how a spring supplies more force—or more *pull*—as you stretch it more and more. You will observe how different springs exert forces of different strengths. Finally, you will test Newton's first law of motion.

MATERIALS

For each student or group:

PART I

- Laboratory stand with an attachable clamp
- Two coil springs of differing stiffness
- Assorted lab weights, 1 to 10 newtons
- Spring scale (reading up to 20 newtons)
- Meter stick
- Vinyl elecrical tape

PART II

- Table tennis or other smooth ball
- Smooth, level floor or table

PROCEDURE

PART I

1. Set up the stand, meter stick, and clamp as in Figure 1. The clamp should be near the top of the stand. Tape the meter stick to the upright part of the stand, with one end of the meter stick touching the base of the stand.

(continued)

Name ______________________ Date ______________

What Is a Force? *(continued)*

STUDENT ACTIVITY PAGE

2. Suspend one of the springs from the clamp. Using the scale on the meter stick, observe the height of the lowermost part of the spring. Record this value in the Data Collection and Analysis section.
3. Choose three objects to suspend from the spring. Weigh these objects using a spring scale calibrated in newtons (N). Record their weights in the Data Collection and Analysis section. If necessary, use vinyl tape to attach the weights to the scale.
4. Hang the *lightest object* on the spring. If necessary, use vinyl tape to attach the weight to the spring. Record the height of the lowermost part of the spring in the Data Collection and Analysis section.
5. Calculate how far the spring was stretched by the weight of the object. Record the change in length in the Data Collection and Analysis section.
6. Repeat steps 4 and 5 with the next lightest, then the heaviest, weights.
7. Now place a different spring on the stand (either a softer one or a stiffer one). Repeat steps 2 through 6 with the new spring.

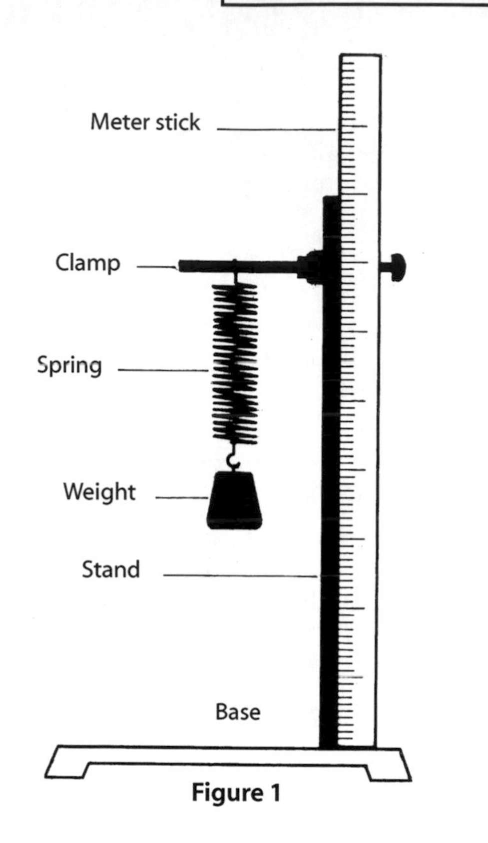

Figure 1

PART II

1. Place the table tennis ball on the floor. If it rolls, find another spot on the floor that is more level. Once the ball is motionless, we know that its speed is zero (0). Therefore, we can assume that there are no forces acting on the ball.
2. Without touching or exerting a force on the ball *in any way*, try to move the ball. Don't touch it with your hand or another object. Don't blow on it or fan the air near it. Don't attach anything magnetic to it. Don't do anything that makes direct or indirect contact. Observe what happens. Record your observation in the Data Collection and Analysis section.
3. Now push gently on the side of the ball with your finger. Again, record your observations.

(continued)

Name ______________________________ Date ______________

What Is a Force? *(continued)*

STUDENT ACTIVITY PAGE

DATA COLLECTION AND ANALYSIS

PART I

Spring 1	Starting Height of Bottom of Spring (Same for All Three Weights)	Height of Bottom of Spring When Stretched by the Weight	Distance Spring Is Stretched (Change in Length)
Weight 1 ______N			
Weight 2 ______N			
Weight 3 ______N			

Spring 2	Starting Height of Bottom of Spring (Same for All Three Weights)	Height of Bottom of Spring When Stretched by the Weight	Distance Spring Is Stretched (Change in Length)
Weight 1 ______N			
Weight 2 ______N			
Weight 3 ______N			

PART II

What happened to the ball in step 2? What did you do to try to move the ball? ______________

____

____

____

Describe what happened in step 3 when you pushed on the ball. ______________

____

____

____

(continued)

Name ______________________ Date ______________

What Is a Force? *(continued)*

STUDENT ACTIVITY PAGE

CONCLUDING QUESTIONS

1. What is the relationship between the distance you stretch a spring and the force it exerts? ______

2. What type of force do these springs exert, a push or a pull? Can you think of a kind of spring that applies the opposite type of force? ______

3. How does increasing the weight of an object suspended by a spring affect the force exerted by the spring? ______

4. What was added in Part II, step 3, that made the ball move (increase speed)? ______

EXTENSION: Take the first spring you used, and choose two more objects as weights. Suspend these objects from the spring, one at a time, to obtain data for five different weights in total. Graph all your data for the first spring. Mark the *x*-axis "weight applied" and the *y*-axis "distance stretched." What is the shape of the graph? Can you predict how far the spring will stretch with a weight you haven't tried? Choose a sixth object, and predict the distance it will stretch the first spring. Test your prediction by actually putting that weight on the spring. How close did you come?

Follow-up Activity

Newton described not just one, but three laws governing the motion of objects. Research Newton's second and third laws of motion. Write a brief report on all three. In your report, describe a simple demonstration of the third law in action.

What Is Work?

TEACHER RESOURCE PAGE

INSTRUCTIONAL OBJECTIVES

Students will be able to

- describe the physical concept of work.
- demonstrate work.
- record data in a table.

NATIONAL SCIENCE STANDARDS ADDRESSED

Students produce evidence that demonstrates understanding of

- properties of matter.
- motions and forces.
- relevant concepts to explain observed phenomena.

Students demonstrate scientific inquiry and problem solving skills by

- identifying and controlling variables in experimental settings.
- working individually and in teams to collect and share information and ideas.

Students demonstrate effective scientific communication by

- arguing from evidence and data.

MATERIALS

For each pair of students:

- Spring scale (reading up to 50 newtons, or 10 pounds)
- Smooth floor
- Supply of books, either hardcover or softcover
- Cardboard box, large enough to fit about ten books
- Meter stick or tape measure
- Masking tape

HELPFUL HINTS AND DISCUSSION

Time frame: 40–50 minutes
Structure: Pairs of students
Location: In class

Try this exercise yourself with the materials on hand before giving them to the students. If no floor or table works well, try using a sheet of plywood or paneling to provide a more uniform surface. Remind students to pull horizontally in step 2, making sure that they do not cause the front edge of the box to rise as they pull. Encourage them to practice pulling on the scale with constant force before they proceed to step 3. When a student pulls the box with the spring scale, the reading on the scale may briefly go higher until the box breaks free of the static friction; then it will settle down to a constant reading as the student pulls slowly and uniformly. Students should ignore the initial high force reading and record the force during steady motion. Both students in a pair may collect common data, but each should do his or her own calculations and Concluding Questions.

ADAPTATIONS FOR HIGH AND LOW ACHIEVERS

High Achievers: Encourage these students to do the Extension and the Follow-up Activity. You can also guide them to texts with a more mathematical treatment of the subject.

Low Achievers: Have reference materials available for these students. Review the relevant concepts such as force, weight, and friction. These students can be paired with high achievers for the activity.

SCORING RUBRIC

Full credit should be given to students who calculate the values of work correctly and who answer the questions correctly and in complete sentences. Extra credit should be awarded to students who do the Extension or Follow-up Activity. The quiz can be scored from 1 to 4 correct.

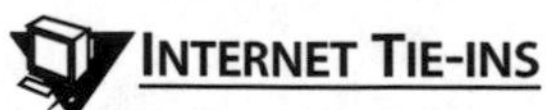

INTERNET TIE-INS

- For more about work:
  http://www.bartleby.com/65/wo/work.html

QUIZ

1. Define *work* as it applies to the field of physics.
2. What will happen to the work done if the applied force is doubled?
3. What will happen to the work done if the distance over which the force is applied is cut in half?
4. True or false: No work is done on a pencil when you raise it above your head.

Name ______________________ Date ______________

What Is Work?

STUDENT ACTIVITY SHEET

BEFORE YOU BEGIN

Three words you will often see on these pages are *force, work,* and *power.* You might think that doing the laundry is a lot of "work." However, in physics, **work** has a very specific meaning.

Think about pushing a book across the table. You exert (apply) a *force* on the book to overcome friction that resists the book's sliding. As a result, the book moves a certain distance. Work (W) is defined as the force (F) exerted on an object, multiplied by the distance (D) traveled by the object *in the same direction as the force.*

$$W = F \times D$$

The amount of work done will increase if the force is increased, if the force acts on the object over a greater distance, or both. Work is done only if something is moved. You might push with all your might against a building and quickly become exhausted, but unless the building moves, no work has been done on it!

Work can also be either positive or negative. If you push a car and it rolls away from you, the work you do on it is **positive**. But say the car rolls downhill toward you and you try to hold it back. You might need to exert exactly the same force on the car. However, since the direction of motion is opposite to the direction of the force, the work done by you on the car is **negative**. That's the same as saying that the car does work on you!

In this activity, you will measure the force you exert to overcome *friction* as you drag an object across a floor. The force of friction increases as the force (weight) pressing the object to the floor increases.

MATERIALS

For each pair of students:

- Spring scale (reading up to 50 newtons, or 10 pounds)
- Smooth floor
- Supply of books, either hardcover or softcover
- Cardboard box, large enough to fit about 10 books
- Meter stick or tape measure
- Masking tape

PROCEDURE

1. Place the cardboard box on the floor. Put three to five books into the box and hook the spring scale to the box. You may need to punch a hole in the box to attach the end of the hook.

(continued)

Name ________________________________ Date ____________________

What Is Work? *(continued)*

STUDENT ACTIVITY SHEET

2. Holding on to the other end of the spring scale, drag the box in a straight line *slowly* across the floor. Make sure the scale reads a constant force in the low half of the scale's range. Reduce the number of books in the box if the spring scale reads too high (off scale). Add books if the scale measures little or no force. Pull *horizontally.* Do not allow the spring scale to lift the box. Only read the force on the scale while the box is moving at constant speed, not when starting up or coming to a stop. Practice until you feel comfortable doing this.
3. Place a small piece of masking tape on the floor at the front edge of the box to indicate the box's starting position. Drag the box a short distance (about a meter) in a straight line, moving the box slowly and keeping a constant force reading on the scale. It should take about 10 seconds to move the box. Read and record the force in the Data Collection and Analysis section. Then, measure the distance traveled by the box and record this value in the Data Collection and Analysis section.
4. Repeat step 3, but this time move the box about twice as far. Try to use the same force as you did in step 3; it should take about twice as long to move the box. Again, measure and record the force used and the distance the box traveled in the Data Collection and Analysis section.
5. Add three to five books to the cardboard box. Repeat step 3 again, and move the box the same distance you moved it in step 3. Measure and record the force you exerted and the distance the box traveled in the Data Collection and Analysis section.

EXTENSION: Repeat step 4. This time, move the box the same distance, but about *twice as fast* as you did in step 4. (That is, move the box about 2 meters in about 10 seconds.) This may require a few practice runs. Measure and record the force and the distance the box traveled in the Data Collection and Analysis section.

DATA COLLECTION AND ANALYSIS

If your scale reads in pounds, convert to newtons (N) by multiplying your reading by 4.45 (1 pound = 4.45 N). If your tape measure reads in inches, convert to meters by dividing your reading by 39.4 (1 m = 39.4 inches). In each line below, use your measured values for force and distance to calculate the work you did in dragging the box. (Multiply the force by the distance: $W = F \times D$.)

Step 3:	force = _______N	distance = ________meters	work = ________N-m
Step 4:	force = _______N	distance = ________meters	work = ________N-m
Step 5:	force = _______N	distance = ________meters	work = ________N-m
Extension:	force = _______N	distance = ________meters	work = ________N-m

(continued)

Name ______________________________ Date ______________

What Is Work? *(continued)*

STUDENT ACTIVITY SHEET

CONCLUDING QUESTIONS

1. Does the work done increase or decrease when you increase the distance the cardboard box is dragged? ______________________________

2. Why does adding books to the box change the result in step 5? ______________________________

3. Does the work done increase or decrease when the force required to drag the cardboard box is increased?______________________________

EXTENSION: In the Extension after step 5, you moved the box at about twice the speed you used in step 4. Did the work done by you on the box also double? Does "work" (as it applies to physics) depend significantly on how fast an object is moved?______________________________

Follow-up Activity

Borrow a spring scale and bring it home. Make a list of at least five ordinary tasks that you think involve work in the physics sense (like putting a stack of clean dishes away in the cabinet). Use either the spring scale or a bathroom scale, and a tape measure or ruler to measure distance. Do each task. Estimate the work done in newton-meters. Next, put your list of tasks in order, from the greatest to least amount of work. (Hints: Keep the tasks **simple** and **safe**. Carrying an *unopened* gallon of paint up a flight of stairs is fine; rebuilding an automobile transmission is not. Also, note that if you hold or slowly lift an object, the upward force you exert on it is approximately equal to its weight.)

What Is Power?

TEACHER RESOURCE PAGE

INSTRUCTIONAL OBJECTIVES

Students will be able to

- describe the physical concept of power.
- understand that higher power does work faster.

NATIONAL SCIENCE STANDARDS ADDRESSED

Students produce evidence that demonstrates understanding of

- motions and forces.
- conservation of energy.
- relevant concepts to explain observed phenomena.

Students demonstrate scientific inquiry and problem-solving skills by

- working individually and in teams to collect and share information and ideas.
- using technology and tools to observe and measure objects.

Students demonstrate effective scientific communication by

- arguing from evidence and data.
- representing data in multiple ways.

MATERIALS

For each pair of students:

- Bathroom or lab scale (range up to 100 pounds minimum)
- Supply of books, wooden blocks, or other small, dense objects
- Stopwatch, or other timepiece that reads seconds
- Cardboard box, as large as student can hold
- Meter stick or tape measure
- Table or desk

Scissors

= Safety icon

EXTENSION:

- Pencil and graph paper, or a computer graphing program

HELPFUL HINTS AND DISCUSSION

Time frame: 40 minutes, or a single period of instruction
Structure: Pairs of students
Location: In class

Advise the students to choose objects that are not fragile or valuable to load the cardboard box. If they don't have enough of one type, it's fine to mix books with wooden blocks, rocks, etc., to reach the desired weight. The final loaded box for each individual should be heavy enough so that he or she must struggle a bit to lift it, but not so heavy as to pose a risk of injury. **Caution: Be sure to instruct all students in the proper method for lifting using their legs and arms, not their backs. Demonstrate this technique to them.** The cardboard box must be strong enough to hold the load of books or other objects—suitable boxes can often be obtained from a grocery or appliance store. We specify a large number of objects (at least 25) because we want to keep the rate at which work is done low when raising the objects individually. If you provide students with a stopwatch to do the timing, you may want to instruct them in its use. If, in step 6, students lift the box too quickly to measure the time it takes with a stopwatch, have them assume and record 1 second for this step.

ADAPTATIONS FOR HIGH AND LOW ACHIEVERS

High Achievers: These students should be encouraged to do the Extension and the Follow-up Activity.

Low Achievers: Review the relevant concepts of force and work. Make sure they understand that the average power is the work done divided by the time taken to do it. These students can be paired with high achievers.

SCORING RUBRIC

Full credit should be given to students whose data recorded in the Data Collection and Analysis section look reasonable, who correctly calculate the work and power in steps 4 and 7, and who answer the questions correctly and in complete sentences. Extra credit should be awarded to students who do the Extension or Follow-up Activity. The quiz can be scored from 1 to 3 correct.

INTERNET TIE-INS

- For more on power:
  http://pc65.frontier.osrhe.edu/hs/science/pwork.htm
  http://www.glenbrook.k12.il.us/gbssci/phys/class/energy/u5l1e.html
  http://www.sasked.gov.sk.ca/docs/physics/u2b3phy.html

QUIZ

1. What is power?
2. True or false: A big, fast motor does more work than a small, slow motor in raising a gallon of water from the bottom of a well. Explain your answer.
3. What are the units of power?

Name ______________________ Date ______________

What Is Power?

STUDENT ACTIVITY SHEET

BEFORE YOU BEGIN

Three words that you will often see on these pages are *force*, *work*, and *power*. A politician might be interested in gaining "power." But in physics, **power** means something different.

Imagine two elevators in a building, of equal size and weight. One is operated by a small electric appliance motor. The other is operated by a big V-8 car motor. Both elevators are raised from the bottom of the building to the top. Their motors are running as fast as they can. In doing so, the motors each do exactly the same amount of *work*. That is, the weight of the elevator times the distance the elevator is raised. But one elevator takes much longer to make the trip than the other. Why is this so?

The answer is that each of these motors is capable of producing a different amount of mechanical *power*. In physics, power is defined as the rate at which work is done, or work per unit time (newton-meters per second, also called **watts**). Mathematically,

$$\text{Power} = \frac{\text{Work (newton-meters)}}{\text{Time (seconds)}}$$

The big car engine can produce far more power than the little electric motor, so it can do the work of lifting the elevator much more quickly.

As you will see, simple machines cannot reduce the amount of work needed to perform a task. They can make it possible for a motor (or muscle) of limited power to do the same amount of work as a more powerful motor, although it takes a longer time.

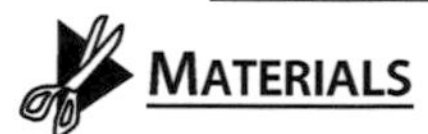

MATERIALS

For each pair of students:

- Bathroom or lab scale (range up to 100 pounds minimum)
- Supply of books, wooden blocks, or other small, dense objects
- Stopwatch, or other timepiece that reads seconds
- Cardboard box, as large as you can hold
- Meter stick or tape measure
- Table or desk
- Scissors

EXTENSION:

- Pencil and graph paper, or a computer graphing program

(continued)

Name ____________________ Date ____________

What Is Power? *(continued)*

STUDENT ACTIVITY SHEET

PROCEDURE

Both students may perform steps 1, 2, and 6 together and share the data. The first student in a group of two should perform steps 3 through 5 and 7 individually. His or her partner will do the timing in step 5. Then the students will trade places, with the second student performing steps 3 through 5 and the first student doing the timing.

Caution: Heavy objects should only be lifted using your legs and arms—*never* by bending over and using your back. Your instructor will demonstrate proper lifting technique.

1. Measure the height of the table, from the floor to the top surface of the table. Convert to meters if you measured in other units, and record your result in the Data Collection and Analysis section.
2. Using the scissors, cut holes in two opposite sides of the box to make handles for easier lifting.
3. Fill the cardboard box with books or other heavy objects until the box becomes difficult but not dangerous for both of you to lift together. If this requires less than 25 pieces, use lighter objects so that the loaded box contains at least 25 individual items. Weigh the loaded box. Convert the result to newtons (1 pound = 4.45 N). Then record your result in the Data Collection and Analysis section.
4. Using the information you collected in steps 1 and 3, calculate the work done in raising the box of books to the tabletop (weight in newtons times height raised in meters). Enter it in the Data Collection and Analysis section.
5. Place the loaded box on the floor next to the table or desk. Place the chair and sit on it so that you can easily reach both the box and the table top. Have your partner time you. Move all the objects in the cardboard box **one by one** from the floor to the top of the table as quickly as you can. When the box is empty, move it to the top of the table also. Your partner should start timing as soon as you begin moving the first book, and end as soon as the cardboard box is on the table. Record the time in seconds in the Data Collection and Analysis section.
6. Put the box back on the floor and return all the items to the box. Move the chair out of the way. With both of you working together, get a good grip on the handles in the sides of the box. Move the loaded box from the floor to the top of the table as quickly as you can without risk of injury. Since both of you will be busy lifting, one partner should estimate the time it takes from the moment the box leaves the floor until it touches the top of the table. You can do this by looking at the timepiece immediately before and after the lift. Record this time in seconds in the Data Collection and Analysis section.
7. From the data you collected, calculate the average power (work done divided by the total time taken to do it) produced during steps 5 and 6. Enter your results in the Data Collection and Analysis section.

(continued)

Name ____________________ Date ____________________

What Is Power? *(continued)*

STUDENT ACTIVITY SHEET

EXTENSION: Machine A and Machine B begin their work at the same time (Time = 0). Look at the data table below. It shows the total amount of work done (in newton-meters) by each machine up to the time it is shut off (Time = 8 seconds for Machine A, and Time = 5 seconds for Machine B). Using the information provided in the table, construct a line graph of total work against time. Plot the data for both machines on the same graph.

EXTENSION DATA TABLE

Time (seconds)	Work Done by A (N-m)	Work Done by B (N-m)
0	0	0
1	1.5	2
2	3	4
3	4.5	6
4	6	8
5	7.5	10
6	9	
7	10.5	
8	12	

DATA COLLECTION AND ANALYSIS

Height of tabletop (step 1) ________ meters

Weight of loaded box (step 3) ________ newtons

Work done to raise the box (step 4) ________ newtons

Total time to raise the individual books and box (step 5) ________ seconds

(continued)

Name ______________________________ Date ______________

What Is Power? *(continued)*

Student Activity Sheet

Total time to raise the full box of books (step 6) ________ seconds

Average power used in step 5 ________ N-m/second

Average power used in step 6 ________ N-m/second

Concluding Questions

1. Is the work done in step 6 greater than, equal to, or less than the work done in step 5? Explain your answer. ______________________________

2. How does the average power produced during step 6 compare with the average power produced during step 5? ______________________________

3. Which felt more physically difficult for you—raising the box of books one at a time in step 5 or all at once in step 6? Relate this to the time it took to raise the books in each step. ______________

Extension: Which machine (A or B) produced the higher power? Relate this to the slope of the graph you drew. Which machine did the most work? ______________________________

Follow-up Activity

During a one-day period, compile a list of all the instances of mechanical power usage that you encounter. This may include elevators, bicycles, nutcrackers—anything in which force is applied, resulting in motion. When you have completed the list, try to put the items in order from highest power to lowest.

How Strong a Nutcracker Is a Door?

TEACHER RESOURCE PAGE

INSTRUCTIONAL OBJECTIVES

Students will be able to

- calculate the mechanical advantage of a lever.
- calculate the force exerted by a door at the jamb.
- demonstrate the use of scientific instruments: spring scale, metric ruler.

NATIONAL SCIENCE STANDARDS ADDRESSED

Students produce evidence that demonstrates understanding of

- motions and forces.

Students demonstrate skill in scientific inquiry by

- working in teams to collect and share information.

Students demonstrate competence with the tools of science by

- using tools to observe and measure with appropriate consideration of accuracy.

MATERIALS

For each pair of students:

- Walnuts (still in their shells)
- Nutcracker (see Figure 2)
- Door
- Cord
- Spring scale with hook (reading up to 20 newtons)
- Meter stick or metric ruler

HELPFUL HINTS AND DISCUSSION

Time frame: 40 minutes, or a single period of instruction
Structure: Pairs of students
Location: In class

In this activity, students will investigate using a door as a lever. Students will measure the force required to crack a walnut with the door by attaching a scale to the doorknob. Students will also qualitatively compare the effort required to crack walnuts using a typical nutcracker and using a door. In addition students will measure the length of the effort and the resistance distances of the door and the nutcracker to determine the mechanical advantage of both. Be certain to **warn the students to avoid getting fingers caught in the door jamb**, and monitor their work for safety.

Be sure students doing the extension know the definition of a class 1 lever (the fulcrum is between the effort force and the resistance force). You can show students that a door is really a seesaw with the board on the opposite side of the pivot bent at 90 degrees.

ADAPTATIONS FOR HIGH AND LOW ACHIEVERS

High Achievers: Have these students assist the low achievers as they calculate the mechanical advantage of both the nutcracker and the door. They should be encouraged to do the Extension and Follow-up Activities.

Low Achievers: These students may be paired with high achievers for the activity. Have these students make the necessary distance measurements to give them more experience using scientific tools.

SCORING RUBRIC

Full credit should be given to students whose data appear reasonable, whose calculations are correct, and who answer the questions correctly and in complete sentences. Extra credit should be given to students who complete the Extension or Follow-up Activities. The quiz can be scored from 1 to 3 correct.

INTERNET TIE-INS

For more on levers:

Questions 1—4 only: http://www.lkwdpl.org/gr4test/ninth/science9.htm
http://learn.lincoln.ac.nz/phsc103/lectures/energy/levers.htm

QUIZ

1. What two things can a simple machine change?
2. What is mechanical advantage?
3. Explain why it's easier to crack the walnut with the door rather than the nutcracker.

Name ______________________ Date ______________

How Strong a Nutcracker Is a Door?

STUDENT ACTIVITY SHEET

BEFORE YOU BEGIN

A simple machine is something that helps you do work by changing either the direction or the amount of force you apply. A door used as a nutcracker, as shown in Figure 1, does both. As you pull the door closed, the spine of the door pushes into the jamb perpendicular to the applied force and crushes the shell of the walnut. More importantly, the force you apply is multiplied by some factor (number). This factor is called **mechanical advantage**. The door is acting as a simple machine called a **lever**.

For a lever like the door, the **effort distance** is the distance between the pivot and the point where you apply a force. The **resistance distance** is the distance between the pivot and the point where the object being acted on (the walnut) pushes back, or resists the motion of the lever. The mechanical advantage is the effort distance divided by the resistance distance. You will take measurements of the door. You will thus be able to calculate its mechanical advantage. And you will therefore know how much the door multiplies your force.

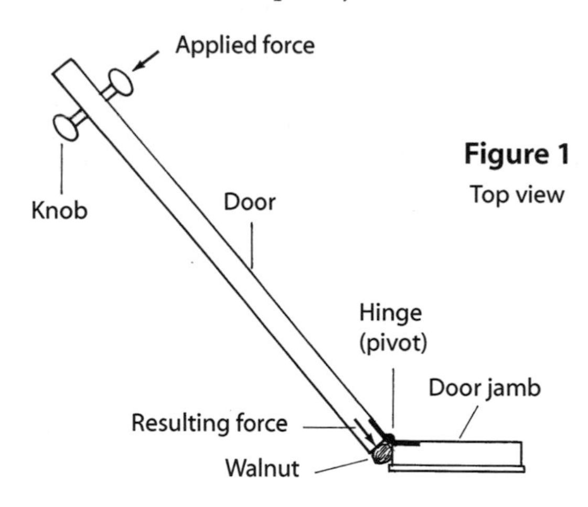

Figure 1
Top view

You will also crack a walnut using a regular nutcracker and take measurements of the nutcracker to determine *its* mechanical advantage. You will see how higher mechanical advantage translates into less difficulty in doing a task.

MATERIALS

For each pair of students:

- Walnuts (still in their shells)
- Nutcracker (see Figure 2)
- Door
- Cord
- Spring scale with hook (reading up to 20 newtons)
- Meter stick or metric ruler

(continued)

Name ______________________ Date ______________

How Strong a Nutcracker Is a Door? *(continued)*

STUDENT ACTIVITY SHEET

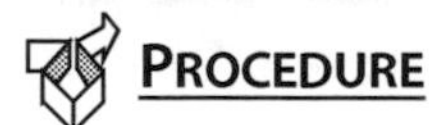

PROCEDURE

1. Using a meter stick, measure the distance between the hinge of the door and the center of the doorknob to the nearest 1 cm. Record it in the Data Collection and Analysis section as the *effort distance.*
2. Tie the cord securely to the doorknob on the side that pulls the door closed. Put a loop on the end of the cord. Attach the hook of the spring scale to the loop at the end of the cord.
3. Put a walnut in the jamb near the hinges and close the door just enough to hold the walnut in place. **Caution: Do not get your fingers caught in the door jamb!** Measure the distance between the hinge of the door and the point where the walnut contacts the door to the nearest 0.1 cm. Record it in the Data Collection and Analysis section as the *resistance distance.*
4. With everyone's hands away from the door jamb, slowly pull the door closed using the spring scale, such that the scale reads the force used in pulling the door. Watch the scale. When the nut *starts to crack,* read the force on the scale. Record the result in the Data Collection and Analysis section. Do not squash the walnut, and clean up if any mess is made.
5. Repeat step 4 two more times, using a fresh walnut each time. Compute and record the average force from the three trials.
6. Calculate the mechanical advantage of the door by dividing the effort distance by the resistance distance. Record it in the Data Collection and Analysis section.
7. Calculate the force needed to crack the walnut by multiplying the average measured force by the mechanical advantage of the door. Record the result.
8. Crack a walnut using the real nutcracker to get a rough idea of the effort required, compared with the effort needed using the door.
9. Measure the distance from the pivot point (arrow A, Figure 2) to the point on the nutcracker's arm where you concentrated the force of your hand (roughly arrow C) to the nearest 0.1 cm. Record it in the Data Collection and Analysis section as the *effort distance.* Some estimation is required here.
10. Measure the distance from the pivot point to the point where the nut makes contact with the nutcracker arm (roughly arrow B) to the nearest 0.1 cm. Record it in the Data Collection and Analysis section as the *resistance distance.*

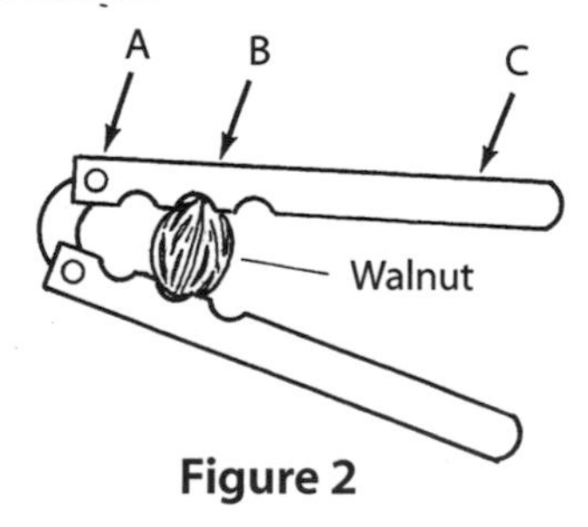

Figure 2

(continued)

Name ______________________________ Date ______________

How Strong a Nutcracker Is a Door? *(continued)*

STUDENT ACTIVITY SHEET

11. Calculate the mechanical advantage of the nutcracker by dividing the effort distance by the resistance distance. Record the result.

DATA COLLECTION AND ANALYSIS:

DOOR	
Width of door to knob (effort distance)	_______ cm
Distance from hinge to walnut (resistance distance)	_______ cm
Applied force (trial #1)	_______ nt
Applied force (trial #2)	_______ nt
Applied force (trial #3)	_______ nt
Applied force (average of trials 1 to 3)	_______ nt
Mechanical advantage of door	_______
Force exerted to crack walnut	_______ nt
NUTCRACKER	
Effort distance (A to C)	_______ cm
Resistance distance (A to B)	_______ cm
Mechanical advantage of nutcracker	_______

EXTENSION: There are actually three "classes" of lever. In a class 1 lever the pivot, or **fulcrum**, is between the effort and the resistance. In a class 2 lever the resistance is between the fulcrum and the effort. In a class 3 lever the effort is between the fulcrum and the resistance. Examine the real nutcracker and the door used as a nutcracker, and determine which class of lever each falls into. Be careful—it might help to redraw Figure 1 with the effort distance and the resistance distance along a single line.

(continued)

Name ______________________ Date ______________

How Strong a Nutcracker Is a Door? *(continued)*

STUDENT ACTIVITY SHEET

CONCLUDING QUESTIONS

1. Describe the relationship between mechanical advantage and the ease with which you can operate a machine. ______________________

2. Why does a door have such a high mechanical advantage? ______________________

EXTENSION: What class lever is the real nutcracker? What class is the door? ______________________

Follow-up Activities

1. You know the force needed to crack a walnut and you know the mechanical advantage of the nutcracker. Now calculate how much force is required from your hands when you use a real nutcracker.
2. Obtain a bathroom scale. Put it up against the wall and push with all your strength. Find the maximum amount of force you can exert against a wall. Multiply *your* maximum force by the mechanical advantage of the door you used. This gives you the maximum amount of force your door can exert against something placed in the jamb. Relate this to safety, especially the warnings in this activity to avoid getting fingers caught in the door jamb.

How Does a Ramp Work As a Simple Machine?

TEACHER RESOURCE PAGE

INSTRUCTIONAL OBJECTIVES

Students will be able to

- calculate the mechanical advantage of an inclined plane.
- calculate the efficiency of a machine.
- demonstrate use of scientific tools: meter stick, spring scale.
- record data in a table.

NATIONAL SCIENCE STANDARDS ADDRESSED

Students produce evidence that demonstrates understanding of

- motions and forces.

Students demonstrate skill in scientific inquiry by

- working in teams to collect and share information.

Students demonstrate competence with the tools of science by

- using tools to observe and measure with appropriate consideration of accuracy.

Students demonstrate effective scientific communication by

- arguing from evidence and data.
- representing data and results in multiple ways.

MATERIALS

***For each group of students*:**

- Spring scale (reading up to 20 newtons)
- Wooden board (about 15 cm × 50 cm)
- Two stands with clamps
- Metal bar or wooden dowel
- Small cardboard box
- 1-kilogram weight
- Meter stick
- 6 feet of string
- C-clamp

EXTENSION:

- Graph paper

HELPFUL HINTS AND DISCUSSION

Time frame: 40 minutes, or a single period of instruction
Structure: Groups of two or three students
Location: In class

In this activity, students will drag a weighted cardboard box up an inclined plane. They will vary the angle of the plane and use a scale attached to the box as they drag it up to study how the amount of force varies with the slope. They will be told how to calculate mechanical advantage for an inclined plane and will do so for each ramp angle they use. Once students measure the force needed they will determine the work input. They can then calculate the efficiency of the ramp at each angle. Students will be able to see that they actually do more work when they use a machine. It is important to review the definitions of **machine**, **work**, and **mechanical advantage** before beginning this activity. It might be helpful to put the required formulas on the chalkboard. The small cardboard box supplied should be no more than 7 to 10 cm on a side. The wooden board should be about 15 cm × 50 cm and can be any thickness so long as it doesn't flex noticeably while supporting a 1-kilogram weight. Be sure the lab stands are tall enough to hold the bar or dowel 30 cm above the table.

ADAPTATIONS FOR HIGH AND LOW ACHIEVERS

High Achievers: Have these students assist the low achievers as they calculate the work done by the machine, the mechanical advantage, and the efficiency. They should also be encouraged to do the Extension and the Follow-up Activity.

Low Achievers: Have these students take all the necessary measurements using the meter stick to give them more experience with scientific tools. They may also work with the higher achievers to do all the calculations.

SCORING RUBRIC

Full credit should be given to students who accurately complete the entries in the data table and who answer the questions correctly and in complete sentences. Extra credit should be given to students who complete the Extension or Follow-up Activity. The quiz can be scored from 1 to 3 correct.

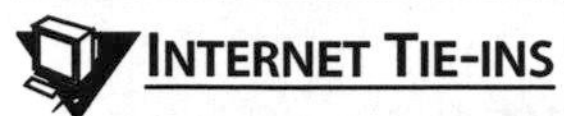

INTERNET TIE-INS

- For more about ramps:
  http://www.uark.edu/depts/aeedhp/agscience/simpmach.htm

QUIZ

1. What is a machine?
2. What is mechanical advantage?
3. Do you do more or less work when you use a machine? Explain your answer.

Name ______________________________ Date ______________

How Does a Ramp Work As a Simple Machine?

STUDENT ACTIVITY PAGE

BEFORE YOU BEGIN

A **machine** changes the direction and/or amount of force you apply. Something as simple as a ramp, also called an **inclined plane**, is called a machine because it allows you to raise an object from one level to another using less force than if you had simply lifted it. Which would be easier: lifting a piano onto a truck or rolling it up a ramp? The ramp is the better choice because you could use less force than the full weight of the piano and still get it onto the truck. This property of a machine is called **mechanical advantage**. The mechanical advantage of a machine is the factor by which the machine multiplies your force. For example, a machine with a mechanical advantage of 5 will put out a force of 50 newtons (N) if you put in a force of 10 newtons. In this activity, you will study the mechanical advantage of an inclined plane. And you will see how it changes as you vary the tilt angle of the inclined plane.

You will also discover that when you use a machine you don't do less work—you do more! **Work** is the amount of energy used to accomplish a task. It is defined as the force used times the distance moved while the force is applied. You do extra work using a machine because you always encounter **friction**. Friction is a force that arises when two surfaces rub against each other (as when you slide a block up a ramp). Friction *opposes* the motion. It turns some of the energy (work) you are using into heat. Friction therefore, wastes some energy, but some machines waste less energy than others do. The **efficiency** of a machine expressed as a percent is a measure of how much (or how little) energy a machine wastes. This is calculated as 100 times the work done by the machine, divided by the work put into the machine. A perfect machine that wastes no energy would have an efficiency of 100 percent. You will study the efficiency of your ramp as a machine.

MATERIALS

For each group of students:

- Spring scale (reading up to 20 newtons)
- Wooden board (about 15 cm × 50 cm)
- Two stands with clamps
- Metal bar or wooden dowel
- Small cardboard box
- 1-kilogram weight
- Meter stick
- 6 feet of string
- C-clamp

EXTENSION:

- Graph paper

(continued)

Name ______________________ Date ______________

How Does a Ramp Work As a Simple Machine? *(continued)*

STUDENT ACTIVITY PAGE

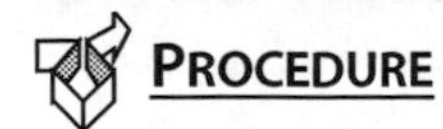

PROCEDURE

1. Attach the bar to the two stands using two clamps. Clamp the bar between the stands, 10 cm off the table, as in Figure 1. Be sure the bar is horizontal.

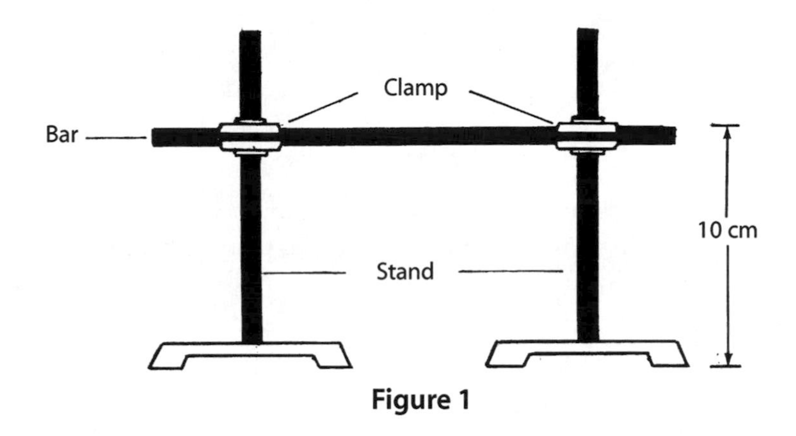

Figure 1

2. Measure the length of your wooden board and record it in the Data Collection and Analysis section.

3. Make a ramp out of the wooden board by putting one end on the table and the other end on the bar, as shown in Figure 2. Have the board extend no more than 1 cm over the bar. Use a C-clamp to attach the board to the bar.

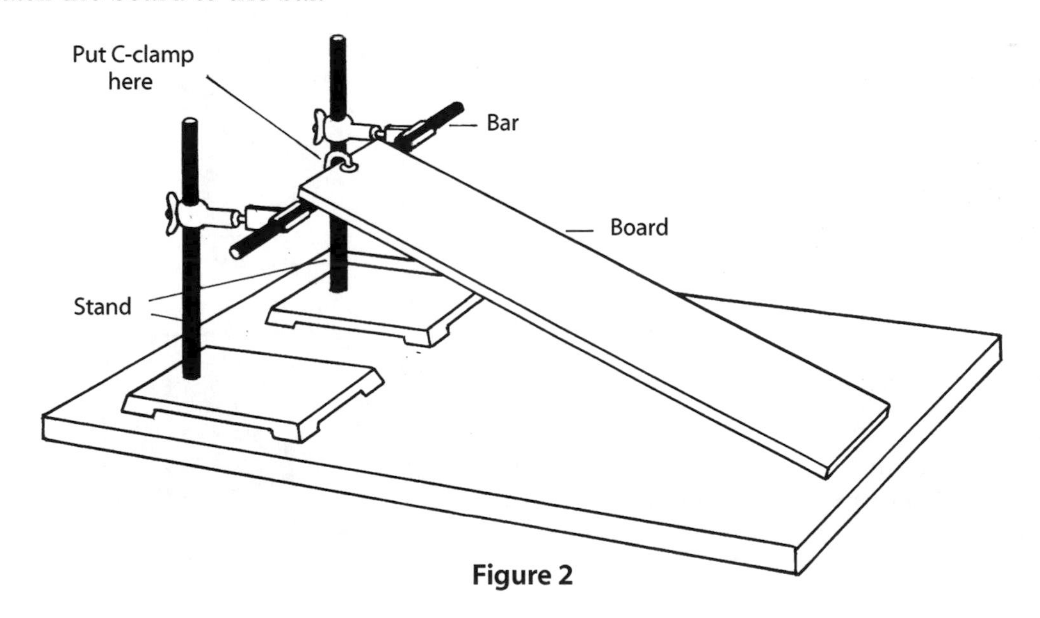

Figure 2

(continued)

Name ______________________ Date ______________

How Does a Ramp Work As a Simple Machine? *(continued)*

Student Activity Page

4. Wrap the string around the cardboard box and tie it. Make a loop in the string on one side of the cardboard box as in Figure 3.

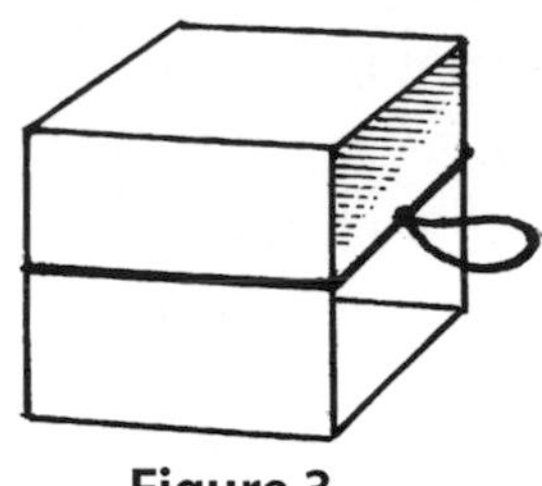

Figure 3

5. Place the 1-kg weight in the cardboard box. Weigh the cardboard box with the weight inside by hanging the assembly vertically from the spring scale (Figure 4). Enter the weight in the Data Collection and Analysis section.

6. Place the box (with the weight) on the board, near the bottom edge of the ramp. Attach the spring scale to the string as you did in step 5. Pull the box up to the top of the ramp by pulling on the scale. Pull slowly and smoothly, parallel to the board, so that the spring scale gives you a consistent reading. This reading indicates the force required to drag the box up the ramp. Record the force in the data table in the Data Collection and Analysis section.

7. Repeat step 6 with the bar at two additional heights: 20 cm and 30 cm. Record the force for each height of the bar in the data table.

Perform steps 8 through 11 for each height of the bar (10, 20, and 30 cm):

8. Calculate the work done by the machine. Multiply the weight of the box with the weight inside (in newtons) by the height of the bar in meters. Record your results in the data table.

9. Calculate and record the work you performed (work input). Multiply the force required to drag the box (in newtons) by the length of the ramp in meters.

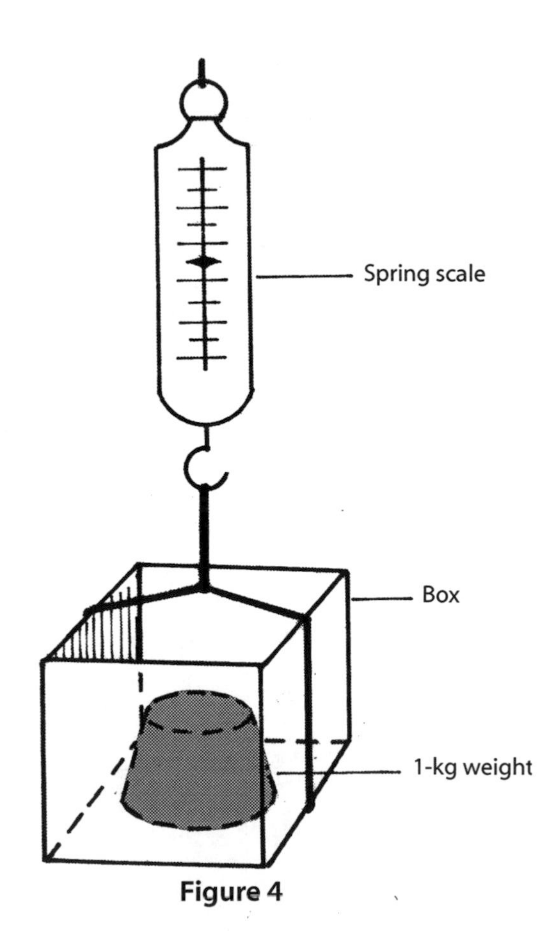

Figure 4

(continued)

Name ______________________________ Date ______________

How Does a Ramp Work As a Simple Machine? *(continued)*

STUDENT ACTIVITY PAGE

10. Determine the efficiency of your machine in the following way. Divide the work performed by the machine (calculated in step 8) by the work performed by you (calculated in step 9). This should be a fraction less than 1.0. Now multiply this fraction by 100 to express the efficiency as a percent. Record your results in the data table.

11. Calculate the mechanical advantage of your inclined plane. Divide the length of the ramp by the height of the bar. Be sure that both are in meters (convert the height of the bar to meters by dividing centimeters by 100). Record your results in the data table.

DATA COLLECTION AND ANALYSIS

Length of wooden board __________ meters
Weight of box with weight inside __________ newtons (N)

DATA TABLE

Height of bar	10 cm = ______ m	20 cm = ______ m	30 cm = ______ m
Force required to drag box (N)			
Work performed by machine (N-m)			
Work you performed in dragging box (N-m)			
Efficiency of machine (%)			
Mechanical advantage			

EXTENSION: On a sheet of graph paper, or using a computer graphing program, plot the efficiency of the three ramps. Plot mechanical advantage on the *x*-axis and efficiency on the *y*-axis.

(continued)

Name ______________________ Date ______________

How Does a Ramp Work As a Simple Machine? *(continued)*

STUDENT ACTIVITY PAGE

CONCLUDING QUESTIONS

1. When the bar is lower, is the force required to drag the box up the ramp higher or lower? Explain your answer. ______________________

2. Does the work performed by the ramp working as a machine depend on the amount of friction between the box and the ramp? Why or why not? ______________________

3. Why do we use machines if they require additional work? ______________________

EXTENSION: What is the relationship between mechanical advantage and the efficiency of the ramp as a machine? ______________________

Follow-up Activity

Very few machines around us in everyday life are made up of one simple machine. That's because putting two or more simple machines together greatly increases either the mechanical advantage or the efficiency. Repeat the experiment you did, but put the box on wheels. Wheels are also machines. Determine how adding wheels changes the efficiency of your machine.

What Mechanical Advantage Do You Have in Your Bicycle?

TEACHER RESOURCE PAGE

INSTRUCTIONAL OBJECTIVES

Students will be able to

- calculate the mechanical advantage of a wheel and axle.
- calculate the overall mechanical advantage of a bicycle.

NATIONAL SCIENCE STANDARDS ADDRESSED

Students produce evidence that demonstrates understanding of

- motions and forces.

Students demonstrate skill in scientific inquiry by

- working individually and in teams to collect and share information.

Students demonstrate competence with the tools of science by

- using tools to observe and measure with appropriate consideration of accuracy.

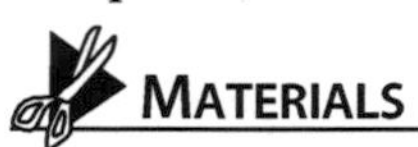

MATERIALS

For each individual or group:

- Bicycle
- Meter stick
- Masking tape

HELPFUL HINTS AND DISCUSSION

Time frame: 40 minutes, or a single period of instruction

Structure: Individuals or cooperative learning groups

Location: In class or at home

In this activity, students will discover how the wheel-and-axle provides mechanical advantage by studying a very common example: a bicycle. You can have a number of students bring in their bicycles, or they can do the activity at home. When your students measure the diameter of the bicycle gears, be careful that they measure to the bottom of the tooth, not the top. Remember that the standard bicycle contains three simple machines working together (making it a compound machine, actually): the pedal crank turning the front gear, the front gear turning the rear gear, and the rear gear turning the rear wheel. **Remind the students to be very careful to avoid getting fingers, hair, or clothing caught in the gears and spokes of the bicycle.** The students perform the measurement of resistance distance three times and take the average of these three trials. This experience can be used to lead in to a discussion of errors and uncertainty in measurements.

ADAPTATIONS FOR HIGH AND LOW ACHIEVERS

High Achievers: Have these students supervise the slower students when they take the measurements to make sure they take them properly. These students should be encouraged do the Extension and the Follow-up Activity.

Low Achievers: Review the concept of an average (arithmetic mean) with these students. Have these students take the measurements with metric rulers to give them more experience using scientific tools.

SCORING RUBRIC

Full credit should be given to students whose data recorded in the Data Collection and Analysis section look reasonable, who correctly do the calculations, and who answer the questions correctly and in complete sentences. Extra credit should be awarded to students who do the Extension and the Follow-up Activity. The quiz can be scored from 1 to 3 correct.

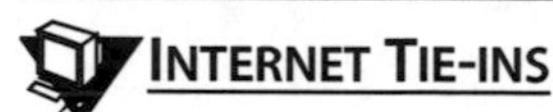

INTERNET TIE-INS

- For more on bicycles:
  http://www.howstuffworks.com/bicycle.htm
  http://www.exploratorium.edu/cycling/

QUIZ

1. Consider a wheel-and-axle simple machine. Which has the larger radius, the wheel or the axle?
2. A machine has a wheel 100 cm in diameter that turns an axle 10 cm in diameter. A rope is wrapped around the axle, and a bucket hangs from the rope. If you turn the wheel to raise a bucket up from the bottom of a water well, what is the mechanical advantage of the machine?
3. The wheel-and-axle is actually a rotating version of another simple machine. What is it?

Name ______________________________ Date ______________________

What Mechanical Advantage Do You Have in Your Bicycle?

STUDENT ACTIVITY PAGE

BEFORE YOU BEGIN

A wheel, or more correctly *wheel-and-axle*, is just a rotating version of a **lever**. The wheel part is a (usually) circular object. The axle is just another circular object attached to the wheel but having a smaller radius. The **mechanical advantage** of a wheel-and-axle depends on which is turning the other. If you turn the axle so that it rotates the wheel, the mechanical advantage is the radius or circumference of the axle divided by that of the wheel. The mechanical advantage is less than one. You get more motion out than you put in, but you also get less force out than you put in. If you turn the wheel instead, the mechanical advantage is greater than one and you get more force out than you put in.

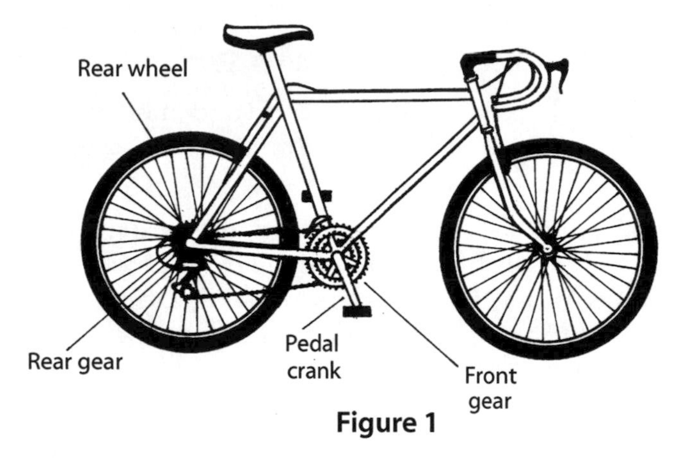

Figure 1

In this activity, you will study a bicycle (Figure 1). A bicycle is a **compound machine** because it has two or more simple machines working together. Just as for a simple machine, the overall mechanical advantage of a compound machine like a bicycle is the ratio of the **effort distance** to the **resistance distance**. You will determine this from measurements.

MATERIALS

For each individual or group:

- Bicycle
- Meter stick
- Masking tape

(continued)

Name ______________________________ Date ______________

What Mechanical Advantage Do You Have in Your Bicycle? *(continued)*

STUDENT ACTIVITY SHEET

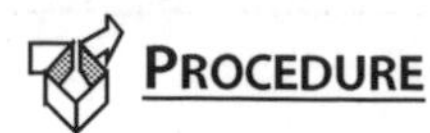

PROCEDURE

If the bicycle you are using has multiple speeds, you will use only the smallest rear gear and the largest front gear. Shift the bicycle into these gears.

1. Using the meter stick, measure the outside diameter of the rear tire, if possible to the nearest 0.1 cm. To get the radius of the tire, divide the diameter by 2. Record your answer in the Data Collection and Analysis section.
2. Measure the diameter of the smallest rear gear. Measure from the bottom of the tooth on one side of the gear to the bottom of the tooth on the other. Divide by 2 to get the radius. Record this in the Data Collection and Analysis section.
3. Locate the center of the pedal crank and the center of the bolt that connects the pedal to the crank. Measure the distance between these points (the length of the pedal crank). Record it in the Data Collection and Analysis section.
4. Place a small piece of tape on the side of the rear wheel and another piece of tape on the floor. Set the bicycle upright on the floor so that the tape on the wheel is directly above the tape on the floor.
5. While turning the pedal by hand, move the bicycle forward until the pedal crank has gone around *one* full turn. Use one of the frame tubes of the bicycle for reference. Start with the pedal lined up with the tube. Stop when it has gone one full turn and is lined up again. Be sure you have gone as close to one turn as possible. Place another piece of tape on the floor where the rear tire now makes contact with the floor.
6. Measure the resistance distance, which is the distance the bicycle traveled between the two pieces of tape on the floor. Record your result in the Data Collection and Analysis section.
7. Repeat steps 5 and 6 two more times. Calculate and record the average resistance distance from the three trials.
8. Calculate the effort distance, which for one turn of the pedal is the circumference of a circle with a radius equal to the length of the pedal crank. To do this, multiply the length of the crank by 2π (6.28). Record this in the Data Collection and Analysis section.
9. Calculate the overall mechanical advantage of the bicycle (in that particular gear) by dividing the effort distance by the average resistance distance from step 7.

EXTENSION: Repeat step 2, but this time measure the diameter of the largest front gear and record its radius. Complete the remainder of the activity (steps 3 through 9) using this measurement. Compare your results with those you got for the smallest front gear.

(continued)

Name ________________________________ Date ____________________

What Mechanical Advantage Do You Have in Your Bicycle? *(continued)*

STUDENT ACTIVITY SHEET

DATA COLLECTION AND ANALYSIS

Outside radius of rear tire	_______ cm
Radius of smallest rear gear	_______ cm
Length of pedal crank	_______ cm
Resistance distance (trial #1)	_______ cm
Resistance distance (trial #2)	_______ cm
Resistance distance (trial #3)	_______ cm
Resistance distance (average)	_______ cm
Effort distance	_______ cm
Overall mechanical advantage	_______ cm

EXTENSION:

Radius of the largest front gear	_______ cm

CONCLUDING QUESTIONS

1. Think of the smallest rear gear of your bicycle as the axle, and the rear tire as the wheel. If you turn the axle so that it in turn rotates the wheel, what mechanical advantage do they have together? What does it mean that the mechanical advantage you calculated is less than one?

____

____

____

____

2. What is the overall mechanical advantage of the bicycle? Is it greater or less than the mechanical advantage of the rear wheel combined with the rear gear? _______________

____

____

____

(continued)

Name ______________________ Date ______________

What Mechanical Advantage Do You Have in Your Bicycle? *(continued)*

STUDENT ACTIVITY SHEET

3. From your experience (assuming you have ridden a bicycle), in which gear is it easier to pedal—the largest rear gear or the smallest rear gear? ______________________

____

____

____

4. You probably did not get exactly the same resistance distance for all three trials. Describe at least two possible sources of inaccuracy. ______________________

____

____

____

____

EXTENSION: There are three wheel-and-axle simple machines involved in pushing a bicycle forward. One is the rear gear turning the rear wheel, which we have already discussed. Identify the other two. Hints: For one of these simple machines the "wheel" part is not a circular object. For the other, the "wheel" and the "axle" are not on the same axis but are connected by another, flexible part of the bicycle. From the measurements you've made, estimate the mechanical advantage of each of these three simple machines. ______________________

____

____

____

Follow-up Activity

Look where the brake pads are positioned on a bicycle. Is that a good place (radius) for the brakes or not? Find out where the brakes are located on an automobile wheel. Is this the most advantageous place for them? What does this tell you about how powerful an automobile's brakes have to be?

How Does a Wedge Make Work Easier?

TEACHER RESOURCE PAGE

INSTRUCTIONAL OBJECTIVES

Students will be able to

- describe the function of a wedge as a simple machine.
- state the mechanical advantage of a wedge.
- demonstrate the reduction in force enabled by using a wedge.

NATIONAL SCIENCE STANDARDS ADDRESSED

Students produce evidence that demonstrates understanding of

- motions and forces; work, friction.

Students demonstrate scientific inquiry and problem-solving skills by

- working individually and in teams to collect and share information and ideas.
- using technology and tools to observe and measure objects.
- identifying problems, evaluating design of investigations.

Students demonstrate effective scientific communication by

- arguing from evidence and data.

MATERIALS

For each pair of students:

- Scrap wood, including thin plywood
- Glue (fast-setting)
- String, about 10 to 15 cm long
- Ruler or meter stick
- Empty plastic food container or small cardboard box
- Assorted weights, stones, nuts and bolts, etc.
- Spring scale (range 0 to 10 newtons)
- Laboratory scale
- Table, bench, or other smooth surface

HELPFUL HINTS AND DISCUSSION

Time frame: 50 minutes, or a single period of instruction
Structure: Pairs of students
Location: In class

We suggest having the students build the wedges out of scrap wood taken from wooden fruit boxes, which can usually be obtained from a supermarket. The boxes we have in mind are constructed from thin (1/8-inch) plywood with short triangular blocks of wood used as reinforcement. Dismantle the cartons and **remove all nails and staples** before giving the pieces to the students. If such cartons are not available, devise an alternate means of constructing appropriate wedges from locally-obtainable materials.

The final wedges should be about 10 cm wide and 30 to 40 cm long and should slope about 1 cm for every 10 cm of length. The shape of the wood block shown in Figure 2 is not important—it may also be square or rectangular. If a slow-setting glue is used you may need to have the students do step 1 a day ahead so the glue has time to set. The plastic container could be, for example, an empty margarine tub. The "laboratory scale" specified may be any type of scale that can weigh a container of 2 to 3 pounds to an accuracy of about 0.1 pound.

The student in each pair who restrains the container in step 5 while the wedge is being pulled underneath may want to practice a bit. The trick is to prevent the container from falling over or moving sideways while allowing it to be lifted by the wedge. The spring scale must be read while the wedge is being moved.

ADAPTATIONS FOR HIGH AND LOW ACHIEVERS

High Achievers: These students should be encouraged to do the Extension and the Follow-up Activity.

Low Achievers: Review the relevant concepts of force, weight, and work. These students can be paired with high achievers for the activity.

Scoring Rubric

Full credit should be given to students whose data look reasonable and who answer the questions correctly and in complete sentences. Extra credit should be given to students who do the Extension or Follow-up Activity. The quiz can be scored from 1 to 3 correct.

Internet Tie-ins

- For more on wedges as simple machines, see:
  http://fbox.vt.edu:10021/D/djoscely/SmplMach/SmplMach.htm

Quiz

1. A wedge is a type of what basic simple machine?
2. True or false: A wedge reduces the force necessary to perform a task by increasing the distance over which the force is applied.
3. What is the mechanical advantage of a wedge 1 cm thick and 6 cm long?

Name ______________________ Date ______________

How Does a Wedge Make Work Easier?

STUDENT ACTIVITY SHEET

BEFORE YOU BEGIN

You may have seen elsewhere how an **inclined plane** (ramp) can make it easier to lift an object against the force of gravity. A ramp converts force or motion in one direction into force or motion in another. Have you ever pushed a shopping cart up a ramp? You exerted a horizontal force on the cart, which raised the cart's height above the ground.

A wedge is an inclined plane that, unlike a ramp, moves when in use. It, too, converts force in one direction into force in another and provides **mechanical advantage**. Like any inclined plane, it does this by applying the lower force over a greater distance. So the total work done (without considering friction) is unchanged.

A splitting wedge is a good example, as shown in Figure 1. Once the wedge is partway into a log, force exerted downward by a hammer becomes a force pushing the two halves of the log outward. This causes it to split further. The wedge moves a distance D for every distance d the pieces of the log move. So the downward force on the wedge only needs to be d/D times the force needed to pull the log apart directly. The ratio D/d is the mechanical advantage of the wedge.

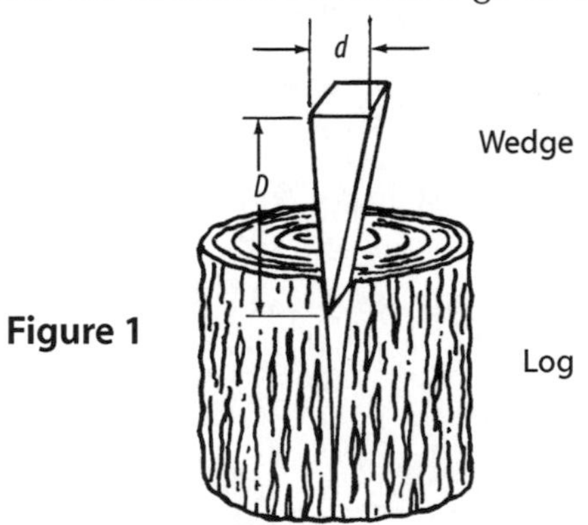

Figure 1

MATERIALS

For each pair of students:

- Scrap wood, including thin plywood
- Glue (fast-setting)
- String, about 10 to 15 cm long
- Ruler or meter stick
- Empty plastic food container or small cardboard box
- Assorted weights, stones, nuts and bolts, etc.
- Spring scale (range 0 to 10 newtons)
- Laboratory scale
- Table, bench, or other smooth surface

(continued)

How Does a Wedge Make Work Easier? *(continued)*

PROCEDURE

1. Use the scrap wood or other materials provided by your teacher to construct a wedge. It shoud be about 10 cm wide and 30 to 40 cm long and have a slope of about 1 cm for every 10 cm of length. Glue (don't nail or staple) the pieces together. An example is shown in Figure 2. Make a small hole through the thin plywood near the low end of the wedge.
2. Measure the distances *D* and *d* as shown in Figure 2, and record your values in the Data Collection and Analysis section. Calculate and enter the ratio *D/d*.

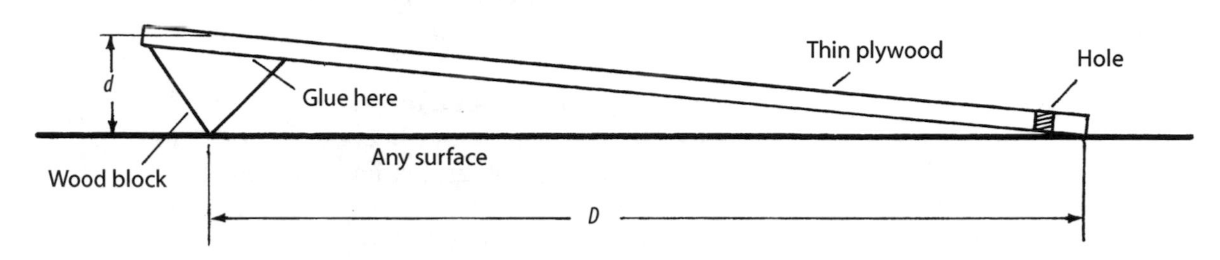

Figure 2

3. Place the plastic container on the laboratory scale. Add small weights to the container until the scale reads 1 kilogram (or 2.2 pounds, or 9.8 newtons, which both correspond to 1 kilogram).
4. See Figure 3. Tie the spring scale to the string, a few centimeters from the wedge. Place the wedge on a table, floor, or bench, with the flat side facing upward. Place the filled container on the low end of the wedge, lined up so it can be pushed up the ramp without falling off to one side.

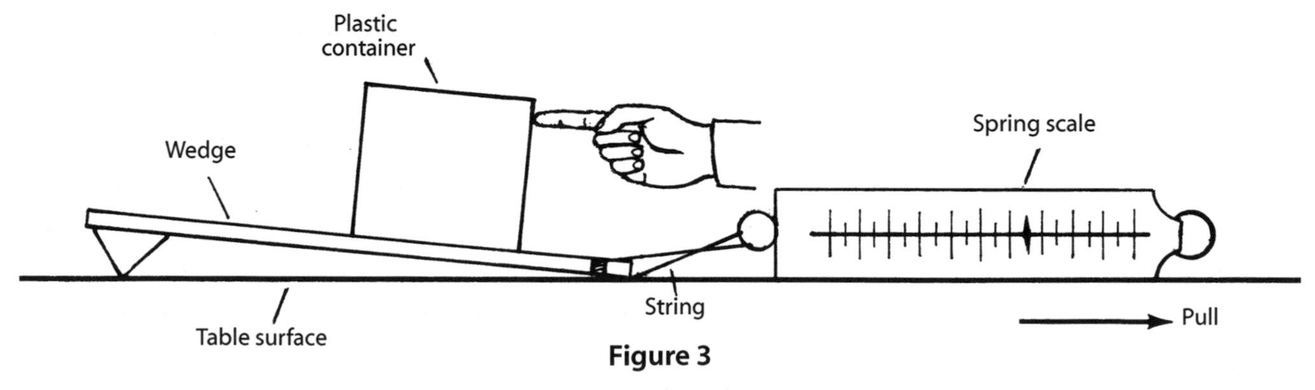

Figure 3

5. Have your partner place his or her hand against the side of the container to restrain it from moving forward or falling off the side of the wedge. Slowly pull the spring scale *horizontally* so that the container begins to slide up the wedge. As the container is being lifted, read the force measured by the spring scale. Record this number in the Data Collection and Analysis section.

(continued)

Name ______________________________ Date ____________________

How Does a Wedge Make Work Easier? *(continued)*

STUDENT ACTIVITY SHEET

6. The weight of the filled container is the force needed to raise it directly, without the aid of a machine. With the aid of the wedge as a machine, you exerted a (presumably smaller) horizontal force and still raised the container. Calculate the ratio (Weight lifted)/(Horizontal force exerted) and enter your result in the Data Collection and Analysis section. Be sure both forces are in newtons.

DATA COLLECTION AND ANALYSIS

Measured value *d* for your wedge	_______	cm
Measured value *D* for your wedge	_______	cm
Calculated value *D*/*d* (mechanical advantage) for your wedge	_______	
Weight of the filled container	9.8	newtons
Horizontal force measured using spring scale	_______	newtons
$\frac{\text{Weight lifted}}{\text{Horizontal force exerted}}$	_______	

CONCLUDING QUESTIONS

1. What is the theoretical mechanical advantage of the wedge you constructed? How did you arrive at this number? ______________________________

____

____

____

2. What is the ratio of the weight of the weighted container to the force required to raise it using the wedge? Is your answer greater than 1.0? Has the wedge made the job of lifting the container easier or harder? ______________________________

____

____

____

3. Is your answer to question 2 about equal to the mechanical advantage of your wedge? If not, why not? ______________________________

____

____

____

(continued)

Name ______________________________ Date ______________

How Does a Wedge Make Work Easier? *(continued)*

STUDENT ACTIVITY SHEET

EXTENSION ACTIVITIES:

1. Suppose you raise the container 1 cm. If you use your wedge, will this require less work, more work, or the same amount of work as lifting it directly? ______________________________

____

____

____

2. How would you improve this activity to make your answer to question 2 come out closer to the calculated mechanical advantage of the wedge? ______________________________

____

____

____

____

Follow-up Activity

There are many wedges in use in the world around us, but some are hard to spot. They are often used a) to cut or break things in half, b) to move things a short distance, and c) to prevent one object from moving relative to another. Carefully observe your environment for a few days, and compile a list of at least ten instances of a wedge used to perform some task. Categorize each as a), b), or c) as described above, or "other."

How Does a Pulley Work?

TEACHER RESOURCE PAGE

INSTRUCTIONAL OBJECTIVES

Students will be able to

- determine the mechanical advantage of a single-pulley system.
- understand the source of inefficiency built into all machines.
- demonstrate use of scientific instruments: spring scale.

NATIONAL SCIENCE STANDARDS ADDRESSED

Students produce evidence that demonstrates understanding of

- motions and forces.

Students demonstrate skill in scientific inquiry by

- working in teams to collect and share information and ideas.
- identifying and controlling experimental variables.

Students demonstrate competence with the tools of science by

- using tools to observe and measure with appropriate consideration of accuracy.

MATERIALS

For each group of students:

- Horizontal bar (6 feet or so off the ground)
- Pail with smooth, firm metal handle
- Small bags of sand or other weights (not to exceed 15 newtons)
- 25 feet of clothesline or other strong cord
- Spring scale with attached hook (reading up to 20 newtons)

HELPFUL HINTS AND DISCUSSION

Time frame: 40 minutes, or a single period of instruction
Structure: Cooperative learning groups
Location: In class

In this activity, students will investigate the use of pulleys by making very crude pulleys consisting of cords sliding over hard surfaces. They will see quantitatively how different cord arrangements provide different mechanical advantage. With the cord thrown over the bar, the bar functions as a crude pulley itself. This is a stationary one-pulley setup with a mechanical advantage of 1. When you tie the cord to the bar and thread it through the pail handle, the pail handle functions as another crude pulley—a moveable pulley. This gives you a mechanical advantage of 2.

The bar should be metal if possible, but may also be wood. We do not describe how to suspend the bar because physical circumstances and available materials may vary greatly from one school to another. **Double-check the knots made by the students to be sure the pail does not slip off and pose a risk of injury.** Since these are poor "pulleys," students will also see firsthand how friction reduces the actual mechanical advantage of machines.

ADAPTATIONS FOR HIGH AND LOW ACHIEVERS

High Achievers: Have these students perform the setup. They should also be encouraged to do the Follow-up Activity. Ask these students what physical objects in the set-up function as the pulleys.

Low Achievers: Have these students perform the actual measurements to develop more confidence with scientific tools and experiments.

Scoring Rubric

Full credit should be given to students whose data appear reasonable and who answer the questions correctly and in complete sentences. Extra credit should be given to students who complete the Follow-up Activity. The quiz can be scored from 1 to 3 correct.

Internet Tie-Ins

- For more on pulleys:
  http://www.howstuffworks.com/pulley.htm
  http://infoplease.lycos.com/ce5/CE042609.html

Quiz

1. What is the benefit of using a one-pulley system that only has a mechanical advantage of 1?
2. What is the mechanical advantage of a one-pulley system that contains two supporting ropes?
3. Why is the actual mechanical advantage always less than theory predicts?

Name ______________________ Date ______________________

How Does a Pulley Work?

STUDENT ACTIVITY SHEET

Before You Begin

As you may have seen elsewhere, a machine changes the direction or the amount of the force you apply, or both. In this activity, you will discover the benefit of a pulley as a simple machine. One pulley used by itself (see Arrangement 1 in Figure 1) has a theoretical **mechanical advantage** of 1. It cannot multiply your force, but it does change the direction. For example, a pulley can enable you to pull down on a rope rather than lift up, which may be more convenient.

You will experiment with crude pulleys consisting simply of cords sliding over a bar or handle in two different arrangements. One arrangement will have a higher mechanical advantage than the other. You will also discover how friction makes every machine inefficient, even the simple ones. So the mechanical advantage we observe is never as great as theory predicts.

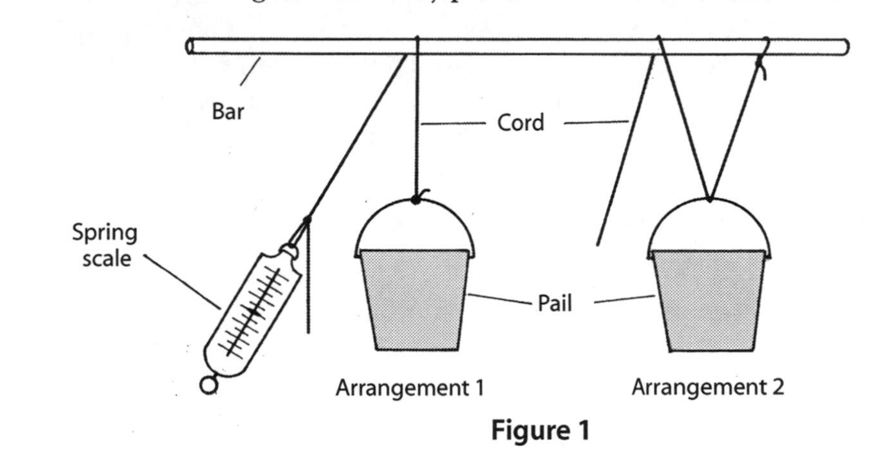

Figure 1

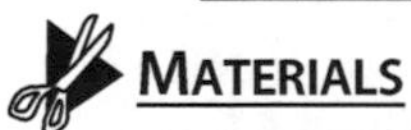

Materials

For each group of students:

- Horizontal bar (6 feet or so off the ground)
- Pail with smooth, firm metal handle
- Small bags of sand or other weights (not to exceed 15 newtons)
- 25 feet of clothesline or other strong cord
- Spring scale with attached hook (reading up to 20 newtons)

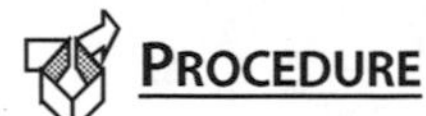

Procedure

1. Load up the pail with about 3 pounds of sand or weights. Using the spring scale, weigh the filled pail. If the pail weighs more than 15 newtons, remove some weight and try again. Record the final value in the Data Collection and Analysis section.

(continued)

Name ______________________________ Date ____________________

How Does a Pulley Work? *(continued)*

STUDENT ACTIVITY SHEET

2. Tie one end of the cord *securely* to the handle of the pail. Put the pail on the floor. Throw the rest of the cord over the horizontal bar. Tie a small loop in the cord near shoulder level on the free-hanging side of the cord. Attach the hook of the scale to the loop. See Arrangement 1 in Figure 1.
3. Pull the scale down slowly and smoothly so the pail is lifted up at constant speed. Read the scale as you are pulling. Record the weight you read there in the Data Collection and Analysis section.
4. Allow the pail to return to its original position and repeat two more times. Record the required force in the Data Collection and Analysis section. Calculate and record the average force needed to lift the pail from the three trials.
5. Calculate the experimental mechanical advantage by dividing the weight of the pail and its contents (the resistance) by the average force needed to lift the pail (the effort) in Arrangement 1.
6. Untie the cord from the pail handle and remove the cord from over the bar. Now tie one end of the cord *securely* to the bar. With the pail on the floor, thread the cord once through the handle of the pail. Throw the rest of the cord over the horizontal bar. Pull the end of the cord until it is taut but does not lift the pail. Again tie a small loop in the cord near eye level on the hanging cord, and attach the hook of the scale to the loop. See Arrangement 2 in Figure 1. Notice that twice as many cord segments support the pail as in Arrangement 1.
7. Repeat steps 3, 4, and 5 for this second arrangement, just as you did for Arrangement 1. Record your results.

DATA COLLECTION AND ANALYSIS:

Weight of pail with sand/weights _______ newtons

ARRANGEMENT 1

Force needed to lift weighted pail (trial #1) _______ newtons

Force needed to lift weighted pail (trial #2) _______ newtons

Force needed to lift weighted pail (trial #3) _______ newtons

Force needed to lift weighted pail (average) _______ newtons

$$\text{Mechanical Advantage} = \frac{\text{Force needed to lift pail}}{\text{Weight of filled pail}}$$ _______

(continued)

Name ______________________________ Date ______________

How Does a Pulley Work? *(continued)*

STUDENT ACTIVITY SHEET

ARRANGEMENT 2

Force needed to lift weighted pail (trial #1) ______ newtons

Force needed to lift weighted pail (trial #2) ______ newtons

Force needed to lift weighted pail (trial #3) ______ newtons

Force needed to lift weighted pail (average) ______ newtons

$$\text{Mechanical Advantage} = \frac{\text{Force needed to lift pail}}{\text{Weight of filled pail}}$$ ______

CONCLUDING QUESTIONS

1. For Arrangement 1, was the mechanical advantage you measured less than, greater than, or exactly equal to 1? Why would there be a difference between the theoretical mechanical advantage and your measured mechanical advantage? ______________________________

2. Compare the measured mechanical advantage for Arrangement 1 and Arrangement 2. What do you think might be the relationship between the number of cords supporting a weight and the mechanical advantage of your pulley system? ______________________________

3. What is the purpose of taking the average of three trials? ______________________________

4. Why do you need to pull slowly and steadily on the spring scale to get the best readings? ______

Follow-up Activity

Repeat this experiment using different types of cord. Discover what types of cord offer the best and the worst mechanical advantage. What is it about the cords that give different results? You can also try looping the cords through the handle of the pail and over the bar once again so that there are two loops of cord supporting the pail. What mechanical advantage does that provide? Report and demonstrate your findings to the class.

What Mechanical Advantage Does a Screw Provide?

TEACHER RESOURCE PAGE

INSTRUCTIONAL OBJECTIVES

Students will be able to

- understand that a screw is a simple machine.
- calculate the combined mechanical advantage of a screw and a screwdriver.
- demonstrate that greater mechanical advantage makes a task easier.

NATIONAL SCIENCE STANDARDS ADDRESSED

Students produce evidence that demonstrates understanding of

- motions and forces.

Students demonstrate scientific inquiry and problem-solving skills by

- identifying and controlling experimental variables.

Students demonstrate effective scientific communication by

- arguing from evidence and data.

MATERIALS

For each student:

- Three different screws (supplied by teacher—see "Helpful Hints" below for size and type)
- Thin plywood boards with predrilled holes (supplied by teacher)
- Ⓢ Screwdriver (flat-bladed)
- Ruler (marked in inches)
- Cloth tape measure (optional)

 = Safety icon

HELPFUL HINTS AND DISCUSSION

Time frame: 20 minutes, or half a period of instruction
Structure: Individuals
Location: At home or in class

Students will be comparing the *relative* mechanical advantage of one screw to another. The mechanical advantage of a screw by itself is not easily demonstrated. A screw is actually a ramp wrapped around a cylinder. A screw with more threads per inch is effectively a ramp with a lower angle and so has a greater mechanical advantage. As with a ramp, a low angle means you travel a greater distance (or turn the screw more times), but can do so with a lower force.

You must supply one of each of the following screws for each student, and mark the heads with different-colored felt-tip markers for identification as follows:

Screw	Color
#10-24 x 1" flathead slotted machine screw	red
#10-32 x 1" flathead slotted machine screw	green
#6-32 x 1" flathead slotted machine screw	black

The first number (#10) specifies the diameter of the screw, the second (-24) specifies the number of threads per inch, and the third (x 1") specifies the length. Be sure to get machine screws, not wood screws or sheet metal screws. The length is not critical, but should not be less than $\frac{3}{4}$". Do not use Phillips-head screws. Make sure the screwdriver supplied has a flat blade and isn't too small or too large for the screws.

You will need to prepare the boards from thin (about $\frac{1}{4}$") plywood, cut to about 3" x 6" or larger, with smooth edges to avoid splinters. Cut-up scraps from old wood paneling are ideal. Drill three holes in each board: two "large" holes using an $\frac{11}{64}$" drill bit, and one "small" hole using a $\frac{1}{8}$" drill bit. If possible, use a drill press. The holes will be straighter and you can drill several boards at once. Do not reuse the holes—good results depend on having clean, identical holes for each student.

This is a short activity, so students who have a screwdriver at home may be allowed to do it there. Others may use extra time after another in-class activity. **Warn the students to be careful to avoid injuring themselves with the screwdriver.** You may recruit a wood-shop class to help prepare the boards. Or extend the activity to a full period of instruction by convening class in the shop and having your students prepare the boards (**with full attention to safety and with the assistance of a shop teacher**).

ADAPTATIONS FOR HIGH AND LOW ACHIEVERS

High Achievers: These students should do the Follow-up Activities.

Low Achievers: Review the ramp as a simple machine and the concept of mechanical advantage.

SCORING RUBRIC

Full credit should be given to students whose data appear reasonable, whose calculations are correct, and who answer the questions correctly and in complete sentences. Extra credit should be given to students who complete the Follow-up Activities. The quiz can be scored from 1 to 2 correct.

INTERNET TIE-INS

- For more about screws:

  http://www.uark.edu/depts/aeedhp/agscience/simpmach.htm

QUIZ

1. How far does a screw move forward during each turn?
2. The mechanical advantage of a screw by itself has little meaning because you always use it with what other machine?

Name ______________________________ Date ______________

What Mechanical Advantage Does a Screw Provide?

STUDENT ACTIVITY PAGE

 BEFORE YOU BEGIN 

As you probably already know, a machine changes the direction or the amount of force you apply. A screw, which can be thought of as a ramp wrapped around a cylinder, does both. As you rotate the screw one full turn, the screw moves forward a distance equal to the distance P between adjacent threads (Figure 1). This distance is usually small, and since you apply effort through a much longer distance, screws give a large **mechanical advantage**. A screw with more threads per inch moves a smaller distance each turn and so has a greater mechanical advantage. In this activity you will compare the *relative* mechanical advantage of one screw to another.

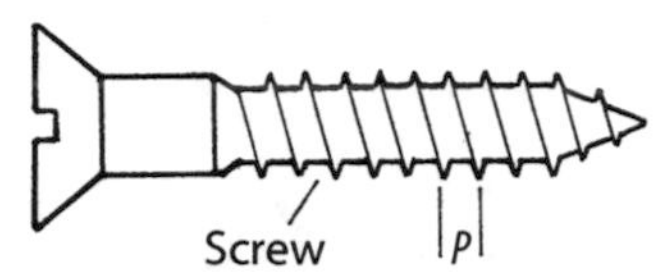

Figure 1

The mechanical advantage of a screw by itself has little meaning. That's because you always use another machine, the screwdriver, to turn it. The screwdriver has its own mechanical advantage. The overall mechanical advantage of a screw plus a screwdriver is equal to the circumference of the screwdriver (the **effort distance**) divided by the distance between threads of the screw (the **resistance distance**). You can measure the circumference of the screwdriver handle directly, or measure its diameter and multiply it by π (approximately 3.14). You will drive each of the screws into a sheet of wood to see which feels easiest to drive in.

 MATERIALS

For each student:

- Three different screws (supplied by teacher)
- Thin plywood boards with predrilled holes (supplied by teacher)
- Screwdriver (flat-bladed)
- Ruler (marked in inches)
- Cloth tape measure (optional)

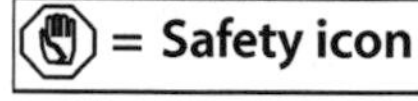

PROCEDURE

Note: All measurements should be in inches.

1. Measure the circumference of the screwdriver handle. If a cloth tape measure is available, you can do this directly by wrapping the tape around the handle. If not, then measure the diameter of the handle and multiply by 3.14. Record your results in the Data Collection and Analysis section.

(continued)

Name ______________________________ Date ______________________

What Mechanical Advantage Does a Screw Provide? *(continued)*

STUDENT ACTIVITY PAGE

2. Select the screw with the red mark on top. Using the ruler, measure the length of the threaded part of the screw. Do not include the head of the screw. On the same screw, count the total number of threads (ridges) along the threaded part of the screw. Count carefully, and double-check. Record your results in the Data Collection and Analysis section.
3. To get the distance between threads, divide the threaded length by the number of threads you counted. To get the overall mechanical advantage of the screw and screwdriver together, divide the circumference of the screwdriver handle by the distance between threads. Record the results of your calculations in the Data Collection and Analysis section.
4. Carefully insert the red screw into one of the two large holes in the board, and screw it in until the board is about at the middle of the screw. Do the same for the green screw in the other large hole and the black screw in the single small hole. Do not damage the holes, and do not turn the screws any more than necessary. **Be very careful not to injure yourself or others with the screwdriver.**
5. Using the screwdriver, try turning each of the screws in or out just one turn, observing how much effort each seems to take relative to the others. Repeat once or twice if you are not sure, but not too many times—the holes will enlarge, making the screws easier to turn but ruining the experiment. Record your impression of which screw (red, green, or black) is easiest to turn, which is hardest, and which is in-between.

DATA COLLECTION AND ANALYSIS

Circumference of screwdriver handle _______ inches

or

Diameter of screwdriver handle x 3.14 to give circumference _______ inches

	Threaded Length (Inches)	Total # of Threads	Distance Between Threads (Inches)	Overall Mechanical Advantage
Red Screw				
Green Screw				
Black Screw				

Easiest _______ (red, green, or black)

Next easiest _______ (red, green, or black)

Hardest _______ (red, green, or black)

(continued)

Name ______________________ Date ______________

What Mechanical Advantage Does a Screw Provide? *(continued)*

STUDENT ACTIVITY PAGE

CONCLUDING QUESTIONS

1. Considering only the red screw and the green screw, which was easier to turn? Is your result consistent with the mechanical advantages you calculated? If not, what might explain the discrepancy? ______________________

____

____

____

2. The green and black screws have the same number of threads per inch. Did you find about the same mechanical advantage for them? Which was easier to turn, and why? (Hint: What force are you overcoming when you turn the screw?) ______________________

____

____

____

Follow-up Activities

1. There are screws of many sizes and shapes throughout our environment. Search through your home or classroom and find at least a dozen examples of screws in use. Make a list of the objects that the screws are part of, the job the screw is doing (for example, "holding the leg onto the chair"), and the type of screw (machine screw, wood screw, sheet metal screw, slotted-head, Phillips-head, flathead, hex-head, etc.) to the best of your ability. If possible, measure and record the diameter and threads per inch of each screw.
2. Screws, bolts, nuts (which are just inside-out screws!), etc., are turned by a wide variety of tools. Investigate these tools and write a short report. Each tool itself is a machine, so in each case identify what kind of simple machine the tool is. If the tool is complex and includes multiple simple machines, identify as many as you can.

How Much Power Do You Have in Your Legs?

TEACHER RESOURCE PAGE

INSTRUCTIONAL OBJECTIVES

Students will be able to

- calculate the work done in climbing a flight of stairs.
- calculate the power generated by their legs in climbing stairs.
- demonstrate use of scientific instruments: stopwatch and metric ruler.

NATIONAL SCIENCE STANDARDS ADDRESSED

Students produce evidence that demonstrates understanding of

- motions and forces.

Students demonstrate skill in scientific inquiry by

- working in teams to collect and share information.

Students demonstrate competence with the tools of science by

- using tools to observe and measure with appropriate consideration of accuracy.

MATERIALS

For each group of students:

- Flights of stairs
- Stopwatch
- Metric ruler or meter stick
- Bathroom scale (or similar)

HELPFUL HINTS AND DISCUSSION

Time frame: 40 minutes, or a single period of instruction
Structure: Groups of 2 or 3 students
Location: In class

In this activity, students will be calculating the power produced by their legs in running up a flight of stairs. In order to do this, they must first calculate the work done and time how long it takes them to do it. Have your students do this by multiplying their body weight by the vertical distance traveled. If they have completed other activities in this book, students should know by now that this is the work they would do if they had in fact traveled vertically. The mechanical advantage of the stairs does not enter into this activity.

Be sure the students use only MKS (meter-kilogram-second) units in their calculations, otherwise their numbers will not come out right.

Be aware of safety in this activity, since students can get competitive. Do not allow more than one team to run the stairs at a time. Parents should be made aware that students will be running up flights of stairs. They should be asked to sign a permission slip and to indicate if there are physical limitations on their child's activities. Some students may be reluctant to have their weight measured—try to have these students act as timekeepers or data recorders. Demonstrate use of the stopwatch.

ADAPTATIONS FOR HIGH AND LOW ACHIEVERS

High Achievers: These students should be encouraged to do the Follow-up Activity.

Low Achievers: Review the relevant concepts of force and work. These students can be paired with high achievers for the activity. Review with them how to do the calculations.

SCORING RUBRIC

Full credit should be given to students whose data recorded in the Data Collection and Analysis section look reasonable, who correctly do the calculations, and who answer the questions correctly and in complete sentences. Extra credit should be awarded to students who do the Follow-up Activity. The quiz can be scored from 1 to 3 correct.

INTERNET TIE-INS

- For more about power:

  http://home.earthlink.net/~dmocarski/chapters/chapter5/main.htm
  http://pc65.frontier.osrhe.edu/hs/science/pwork.htm

QUIZ

1. True or false: A certain amount of work takes twice as long to do if half as much power is used to do it.
2. Does the motor of an elevator taking Mr. Jones from the third to the 8th floor do more work than Mr. Jones climbing the stairs from the 3rd to the 8th floor (excluding the work done moving the weight of the elevator itself)? Explain your answer.
3. Does a machine make a person more powerful? Explain your answer.

Name ______________________________ Date ________________

How Much Power Do You Have in Your Legs?

STUDENT ACTIVITY PAGE

BEFORE YOU BEGIN

You may recall that a machine changes the direction and/or the amount of the force you must apply to perform a task. In this activity, a flight of stairs acts as a machine because it allows your legs to use less force to lift your mass than if you climbed a vertical ladder. A flight of stairs is just an inclined plane with steps cut into it.

When we discuss machines (like your legs or the stairs) we talk not only about the amount of work they do, but how fast they can do the work. The speed with which work is performed is called **power**. This is calculated as work per unit of time. The less time it takes to do the same amount of work, the more power is produced.

In this activity, you will calculate the work that you do when you climb a flight of stairs. The work you perform will be found by multiplying your body weight by the vertical distance you travel. When you use a machine you don't do *less* work. It only seems easier because the stairs allow your legs to use less force. You will measure the time it took to climb the stairs and calculate the power you used by dividing the work done by the time taken to do it.

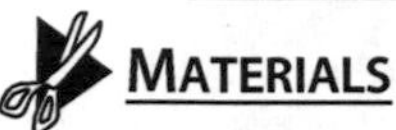

MATERIALS

For each group of students:

- Flights of stairs
- Stopwatch
- Metric ruler or meter stick
- Bathroom scale (or similar)

PROCEDURE

1. Before you begin this activity, select one member of your group to be the runner and another to be the timekeeper. The other student (or the timekeeper) should enter the data and do the calculations. Be sure to record your measurements and calculations in the spaces provided in the Data Collection and Analysis section.
2. Use the scale to weigh the runner. Enter the runner's weight in the Data Collection and Analysis section. Convert this value to newtons (N).
3. Have your teacher take you to the staircase you will use. The runner will run up *one* flight of this staircase.
4. Using the metric ruler, measure the height of one step to the nearest 0.1 cm and enter it in the Data Collection and Analysis section. Convert this value to meters.
5. Count and record the number of steps in the flight of stairs.
6. Under the supervision of your teacher or another adult, have the runner run up the flight of stairs as fast as he or she can safely. **Do not run up the stairs so fast that you risk tripping and injuring yourself.** The timer should time the run to the nearest 0.1 second. The time should be entered in the Data Collection and Analysis section.
7. Complete the remaining calculations in the Data Collection and Analysis section.

(continued)

Name ______________________________ Date ______________

How Much Power Do You Have in Your Legs? *(continued)*

STUDENT ACTIVITY PAGE

DATA COLLECTION AND ANALYSIS

Runner's weight	_______ lbs
Convert weight to newtons (multiply lbs. by 4.45)	_______ newtons
Height of one step	_______ cm
Convert height to meters(divide cm by 100)	_______ m
Number of steps in one flight	_______ steps
Time taken to climb stairs	_______ sec
Vertical distance traveled (# of steps per flight × height of one step)	_______ m

CALCULATING WORK PERFORMED

The work (in N-m, or joules) done in climbing the flight of stairs will be equal to your body weight (in newtons) multiplied by the total vertical distance traveled (in meters):

Work = weight × distance = _______ joules

CALCULATING THE POWER OF YOUR LEGS

Power is equal to work divided by time. The unit of power we commonly use is the joule per second (joule/sec), also known as the watt:

$$\text{Power} = \frac{\text{Work}}{\text{Time}} =$$ _______ watts

The unit of power in the English system is the horsepower. One horsepower is equal to 746 watts. To find out your power in horsepower, divide the power in watts by 746.

$$\text{Power (hp)} = \frac{\text{Power (watts)}}{746} =$$ _______ horsepower

(continued)

Name ______________________________ Date ______________

How Much Power Do You Have in Your Legs? *(continued)*

STUDENT ACTIVITY PAGE

CONCLUDING QUESTIONS

1. If all the power your legs produce were converted to electricity, could you fully light a typical, 60-watt, incandescent light bulb? ______________________________

2. Do you think the unit of horsepower was based on the power produced by an actual horse? Why or why not? ______________________________

3. In the Data Collection and Analysis section you estimated the work done in climbing the stairs by doing a calculation. If the stairs were steeper, would you have done more work? Why or why not? ______________________________

Follow-up Activity

To appreciate how much work it takes to lose weight, calculate how many calories you burned off in climbing that flight of stairs. One calorie is equal to about 4200 joules. Also calculate how many flights of stairs you would have to climb to burn off one pound of fat, or about 4000 calories!

How Can a Class 1 Lever Work As a Catapult?

INSTRUCTIONAL OBJECTIVES

Students will be able to

- calculate the mechanical advantage of a class 1 lever.
- describe how a class 1 lever can be used from either end.
- qualitatively predict the effect of a change in fulcrum position.

NATIONAL SCIENCE STANDARDS ADDRESSED

Students produce evidence that demonstrates understanding of

- motions and forces.

Students demonstrate skill in scientific inquiry by

- working in teams to collect and share information.

Students demonstrate competence with the tools of science by

- using tools to observe and measure with appropriate consideration of accuracy.

MATERIALS

For each pair of students:

- Table tennis ball
- Bottle cap
- 12-inch wooden ruler with both inch and centimeter markings
- Adhesive putty
- Round pencil (not hexagonal)
- Meter stick
- Masking or other tape
- Protective eyewear for both students

EXTENSION:

- Graph paper

HELPFUL HINTS AND DISCUSSION

Time frame: 40 minutes, or a single period of instruction
Structure: Pairs of students
Location: In class

In this activity, students will investigate how a reverse class 1 lever works as a catapult. They will launch a table tennis ball by slapping the short end of a class 1 lever with an open hand. Done with care, this produces more consistent results than dropping a weight on the end of the lever. Encourage your students to practice before taking actual data. Students will then record how high the ball is catapulted. **Caution students not to let the ruler go flying. Tell them to keep their hands on the ruler at the end of the slap. Have them wear protective eyewear.**

Students will see how varying the ratio of the effort distance to the resistance distance produces different velocities, and therefore different heights. Since there are factors that may cause significant variations, the students are asked to do each experiment three times and average the results. If possible, supply your students with 30-cm rulers with a small ($\frac{1}{4}$–$\frac{3}{8}$ inch) hole drilled through at the 1-cm mark. This will eliminate the need for step 3, along with the adhesive putty and bottle cap or washer.

ADAPTATIONS FOR HIGH AND LOW ACHIEVERS

High Achievers: Have these students assist the lower achieving students in taking the data accurately. Encourage them to do the Extension and the Follow-up Activity.

Low Achievers: These students may be paired with high achievers for the activity. Have these students make the necessary distance measurements to give them more experience using scientific tools.

SCORING RUBRIC

Full credit should be given to students whose data recorded in the Data Collection and Analysis section look reasonable, who correctly do the calculations, and who answer the questions correctly and in complete sentences. Extra credit should be awarded to students who do the Extension and Follow-up Activity. The quiz can be scored from 1 to 3 correct.

INTERNET TIE-INS

- For more about levers:

  http://www.lkwdpl.org/gr4test/ninth/science9.htm (1–4 only)
  http://learn.lincoln.ac.nz/phsc103/lectures/energy/levers.htm

QUIZ

1. True or false: A machine can be used to increase, but not decrease, force.
2. The lever used as a catapult in this activity increases distance or velocity. What does a class 1 lever increase when used normally?
3. What is the mechanical advantage of a lever, in terms of effort distance and resistance distance?

Name ______________________ Date ______________

How Can a Class 1 Lever Work As a Catapult?

STUDENT ACTIVITY PAGE

 BEFORE YOU BEGIN 

A machine changes the direction or the amount of force you apply. Often, a machine is used to increase force, reducing the force *you* need to exert to perform a task. The **mechanical advantage** is greater than 1. Sometimes, though, a machine is used in a way that increases the distance an object is moved or the speed at which it travels. When you use a machine in this way, the mechanical advantage is less than 1, and you must actually exert more force than without the machine.

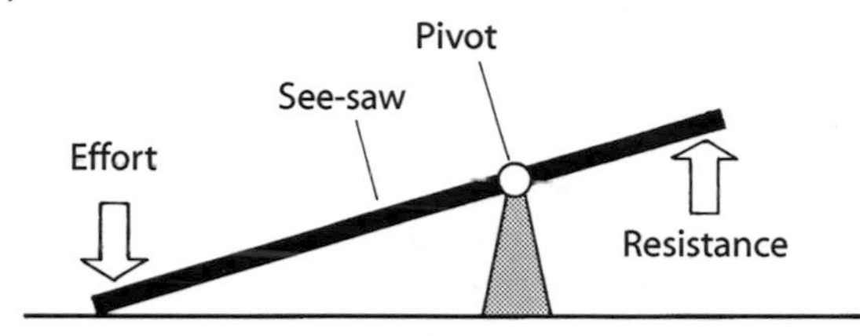

Figure 1

In this activity you will investigate the properties of a class 1 lever used backward to create a simple version of an old-fashioned catapult. A class 1 lever like a see-saw (Figure 1) has its pivot between the effort and resistance. When you push down on one end with enough force (the effort), the resistance (whatever is pushing down on the other end) moves in the opposite direction. The mechanical advantage is the **effort distance** (between the effort and the pivot) divided by the **resistance distance** (between the pivot and the resistance). In this activity you will make the effort distance less than the resistance distance. In doing so, you will use this lever in such a way that the mechanical advantage is less than 1—sometimes much less than 1! What good is that? In this case you are moving a table tennis ball, which is so light that you don't need to multiply your force to get it moving. What you *do* need is to increase the distance you push it. That gives it a greater **velocity** and thus launches it higher.

 MATERIALS

For each pair of students:

- Table tennis ball
- Bottle cap
- 12-inch wooden ruler with metric markings
- Adhesive putty
- Round pencil (not hexagonal)
- Meter stick
- Masking or other tape
- Protective eyewear for both students

EXTENSION:

- Graph paper

(continued)

Name ______________________________ Date ______________

How Can a Class 1 Lever Work As a Catapult? *(continued)*

STUDENT ACTIVITY PAGE

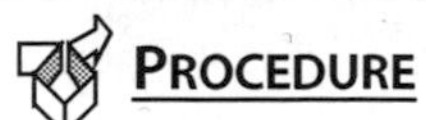

PROCEDURE

1. Set up the meter stick to stand vertically on a table, desk, or bench. Hold it in place by taping it to a wall or nearby object. The **0** (zero) end of the meter stick should touch the table.
2. Using a small amount of adhesive putty, attach the pencil crosswise to the ruler. At first, place the pencil, which acts as a pivot or **fulcrum**, at the 15-cm mark.
3. (Only perform this step if the ruler supplied by the teacher does *not* have a hole through it at the 1-cm mark.) You will need a way to hold the table tennis ball steady for launching. Using a small amount of adhesive putty, attach the bottle cap ("cup" side up) to the upper surface of the 12-inch ruler at the 1-cm mark. This will make the resistance distance 15 cm – 1 cm = 14 cm.
4. As shown in Figure 2, place the ruler on the table near the vertical meter stick, with the pencil down. Rest the table tennis ball in the hole, bottle cap, or washer at the 1-cm mark. Have your partner positioned to see both the vertical meter stick and the launched table tennis ball.
5. Put on the protective eyewear. With an open hand, slap the end of the ruler opposite the ball down with the tips of your fingers. **Caution: Do not let the ruler fly away and injure someone.** Try to concentrate the force of your slap near the 29-cm mark on the ruler. You may want to practice doing this consistently. Using the vertical meter stick as a reference, have your partner observe the height reached by the bottom of the table tennis ball. Record the result under trial 1 in the Data Collection and Analysis section. This will make the effort distance 29 cm – 15 cm = 14 cm.

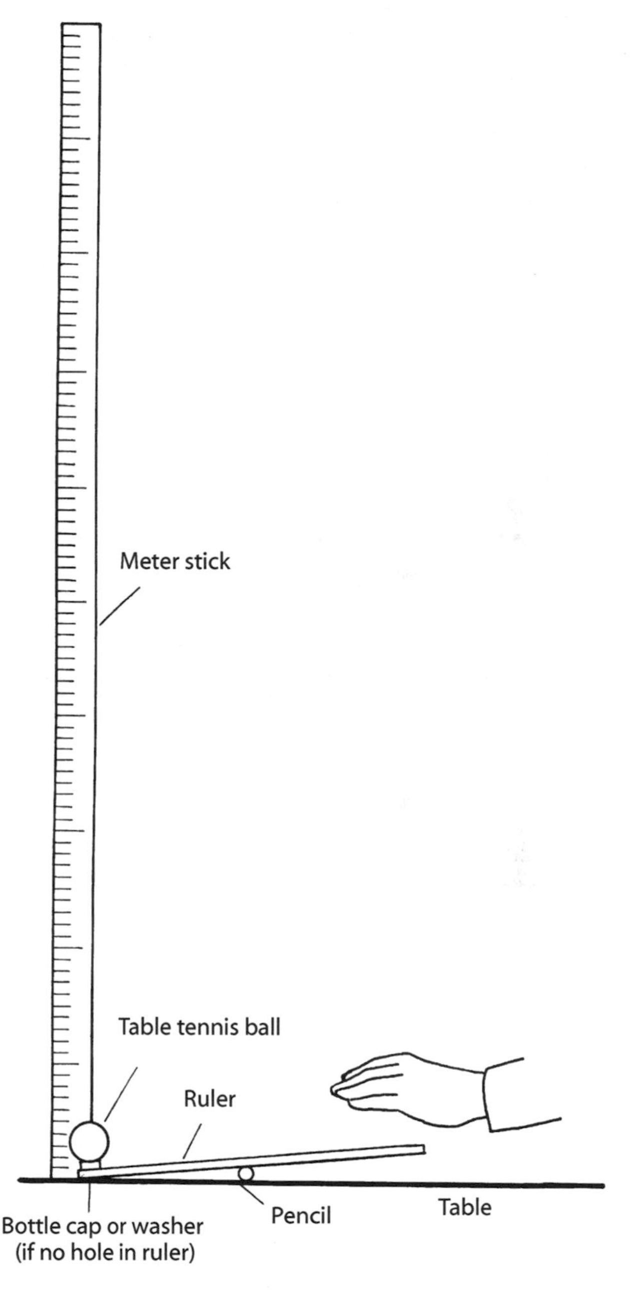

Figure 2

(continued)

Name ______________________ Date ______________

How Can a Class 1 Lever Work As a Catapult? *(continued)*

STUDENT ACTIVITY PAGE

6. Repeat step 5 two more times. Record your results as trial 2 and trial 3.
7. Move the pencil to the 25-cm mark and repeat steps 5 and 6. Record your results.
8. Move the pencil to the 27-cm mark and repeat steps 5 and 6. Record your results.
9. For each pencil position, compute and record the average height reached by the ball in the three trials. Record your results under "Avg." in the Data Collection and Analysis section.
10. Complete the data table by calculating and entering the resistance distance (pencil position minus 1cm), effort distance (29 cm minus pencil position), and mechanical advantage (effort distance divided by resistance distance) for each position of the pencil.

EXTENSION: Make a graph of the data in your table, using mechanical advantage as the *x*-axis and average height launched as the *y*-axis. Choose two more pencil positions between 20 and 28 cm. Repeat steps 5, 6, and 9 with the pencil at these positions and add the data to the graph

DATA COLLECTION AND ANALYSIS

DATA TABLE

Pencil Position	Resistance Distance	Effort Distance	Mechanical Advantage	Height of Launched Ball			
				Trial 1	Trial 2	Trial 3	Avg.
15 cm	15 – 1 = 14 cm	29 – 15 = 14 cm	14/14 = 1.0				
25 cm							
27 cm							
____ cm							
____ cm							

(continued)

Name ______________________________ Date ____________________

How Can a Class 1 Lever Work As a Catapult? *(continued)*

STUDENT ACTIVITY PAGE

CONCLUDING QUESTIONS

1. Compare the average height of the launched table tennis ball to the mechanical advantage for each pencil position. As mechanical advantage decreases, does the height reached increase, decrease, or remain the same? Why? ______________________________

2. You probably observed some variation in the height reached by the ball from one trial to another, even when the conditions (like pencil position) have not been intentionally changed. What is the most likely source of such variation? ______________________________

EXTENSION:

1. Do the data points on your graph make a roughly straight, or noticeably bent, line? Discuss some possible reasons for this. ______________________________

Follow-up Activity

Research the catapults constructed in ancient cultures. Make a diagram illustrating how one worked. Look at a number of designs for catapults. What supplied the force? Were the catapults really simple levers like the one you created? What were they capable of in terms of maximum range and the weight the projectile could throw? Build a small, non-working model of one for extra credit.

What Mechanical Advantage Do Stairs Provide?

TEACHER RESOURCE PAGE

INSTRUCTIONAL OBJECTIVES

Students will be able to

- calculate the mechanical advantage of a flight of stairs.
- calculate the effort force of one's legs when using a flight of stairs.

NATIONAL SCIENCE STANDARDS ADDRESSED

Students produce evidence that demonstrates understanding of

- motions and forces.

Students demonstrate competence with the tools of science by

- using tools to observe and measure with appropriate consideration of accuracy.

MATERIALS

For each student:

- Flight of stairs
- Metric ruler or meter stick
- Bathroom scale

HELPFUL HINTS AND DISCUSSION

Time frame: 40 minutes, or a single period of instruction
Structure: Individuals
Location: At home and other locations

In this activity, students will investigate why it is easier to use stairs than a ladder to travel vertically. Using a vertical ladder requires one's legs to generate a force equal to one's full body weight, while using stairs requires a much lower force. Students will take simple measurements of a flight of stairs and then calculate the mechanical advantage of the stairs. That will enable them to calculate the actual force that their legs exert in climbing the stairs.

Make certain you define a machine. Be sure that students also understand a flight of stairs as an example of an inclined plane. Some students may be reluctant to have their weight known. If you suspect this might be a problem, discourage sharing of data in this activity, or allow students to use a fictitious weight.

Note that while in most activities we specify MKS (meter-kilogram-second) units, it is all right to use pounds for the students' weight since we only want them to understand that the stairs lower the needed force.

ADAPTATIONS FOR HIGH AND LOW ACHIEVERS

High Achievers: Ask high achievers an additional question: Why do the muscles of your legs have to exert more force than will be calculated? These students should be encouraged to do the Follow-up Activity and its Extension.

Low Achievers: Review the relevant concepts of force and mechanical advantage with these students. Have them take the measurements using the ruler to give them more experience with scientific tools. Review with them how to do the calculations.

SCORING RUBRIC

Full credit should be given to students whose data recorded in the Data Collection and Analysis section look reasonable, who correctly do the calculations, and who answer the questions correctly and in complete sentences. Extra credit should be awarded to students who do the Follow-up Activity and its Extension. The quiz can be scored from 1 to 2 correct.

INTERNET TIE-INS

- For more about ramps:
  http://home.earthlink.net/~dmocarski/chapters/chapter5/main.htm

QUIZ

1. What is the purpose of a machine?
2. Why is walking up a steep hill more tiring than walking up a gently sloping hill?

Name ______________________ Date ______________

What Mechanical Advantage Do Stairs Provide?

STUDENT ACTIVITY PAGE

 **BEFORE YOU BEGIN** 

You probably already know that it is easier to climb a flight of stairs to a given height than it is to climb a ladder to the same height. This is because a flight of stairs is actually a **machine**. You can think of a flight of stairs as an **inclined plane** (or ramp) with steps cut into it. As you may remember, a machine changes either the direction or the amount of a force you apply. In the case of stairs, the ramp multiplies the force of your legs, so you don't have to use as much force. This is called **mechanical advantage**. This mechanical advantage is not free, however. In payment you must travel a greater distance walking diagonally up the steps than if you had gone straight up on a vertical ladder. In this activity, you will calculate the mechanical advantage of the stairs. You will also calculate the actual force your legs have to exert in climbing a flight of stairs.

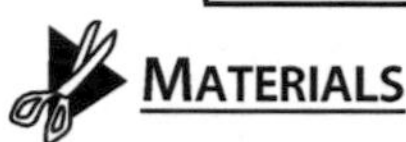

MATERIALS

For each student:

- Flight of stairs
- Metric ruler or meter stick
- Bathroom scale

PROCEDURE

1. Find your weight in pounds and record it in the Data Collection and Analysis section.
2. Locate a flight of stairs.
3. Using a metric ruler, measure the height *H* of one step to the nearest 0.1 cm and record this information in the Data Collection and Analysis section.
4. Measure the diagonal distance *D* between the front edge of one step and the front edge of the next higher or lower step, also to the nearest 0.1 cm. Record this distance in the Data Collection and Analysis section.

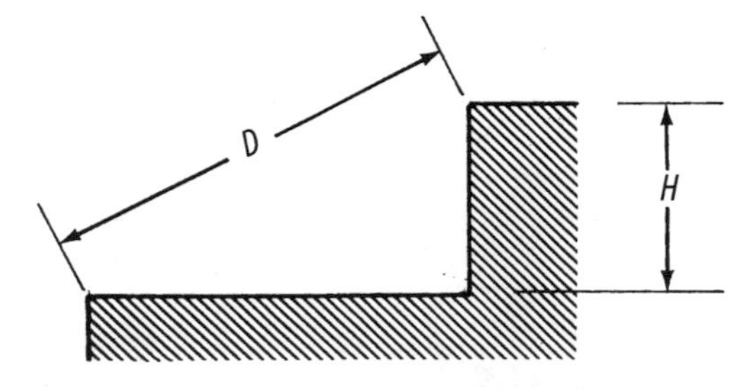

Figure 1

(continued)

Name ______________________________ Date ____________________

What Mechanical Advantage Do Stairs Provide? *(continued)*

STUDENT ACTIVITY PAGE

DATA COLLECTION AND ANALYSIS

Body weight _______ lbs.

Height of one step _______ cm

Diagonal distance between steps _______ cm

CALCULATING MECHANICAL ADVANTAGE

Machines increase (or decrease) the force you exert by multiplying it by some number. That number is called the *mechanical advantage* of a machine. In the case of an inclined plane, you find the mechanical advantage by dividing the length of the ramp by the height the ramp raises you to. Similarly, for a flight of stairs you determine the mechanical advantage by dividing the distance you travel diagonally up the step by the height of the step:

$$\text{Mechanical advantage} = \frac{\text{diagonal distance}}{\text{height}} = \underline{\qquad\qquad}$$

CALCULATING FORCE OF LEGS

Without the help of a machine, the force your legs must produce to lift you is equal to your body weight. With the stairs, the force needed is lower than your body weight.

$$\text{Force of legs} = \frac{\text{body weight}}{\text{mechanical advantage}} = \underline{\qquad\qquad}\ \text{lbs.}$$

CONCLUDING QUESTIONS

1. Why do we build stairs rather than vertical ladders between floors of a building? ______________

____

____

2. Are you surprised by the value of the mechanical advantage provided by the flight of stairs? Why or why not? ____

____

____

3. For a machine to make a task easier, should it have a mechanical advantage less than or greater than 1? Explain your answer. ____

____

____

____

(continued)

Name ______________________ Date ______________

What Mechanical Advantage Do Stairs Provide? *(continued)*

STUDENT ACTIVITY PAGE

Follow-up Activity

Visit stairways in a variety of buildings (old buildings, new buildings, homes, government offices, etc.) and take the same measurements of their stairs. Calculate and record the mechanical advantage provided by each stairway. Compute also the average mechanical advantage of all the stairways in your survey.

EXTENSION: The mechanical advantage you find for various stairways will vary. While doing the survey in the Follow-up Activity, record the age (old or new) and type (residence or workplace) of building along with the mechanical advantage of the stairway. Consider a building built or renovated after 1960 to be "new." Is the mechanical advantage different for residences compared to workplaces? Is the mechanical advantage different for new buildings compared to old buildings? You may have with visit a large number of stairways to see clear trends. Can you think of reasons for your findings?

How Can You Harness the Power of Wind with a Simple Machine?

TEACHER RESOURCE PAGE

INSTRUCTIONAL OBJECTIVES

Students will be able to

- understand the blades of a windmill as simple machines.
- demonstrate the effect of varying the angle of a windmill's blades.

NATIONAL SCIENCE STANDARDS ADDRESSED

Students produce evidence that demonstrates understanding of

- motions and forces.

Students demonstrate skill in scientific inquiry by

- working individually and in teams to collect and share information.

Students demonstrate competence with the tools of science by

- using tools to observe and measure with appropriate consideration of accuracy.

MATERIALS

For each student:

- Thin cardboard sheet
- Unsharpened pencil with eraser
- Glue stick
- Pushpin
- Scissors
- Marker
- Masking tape
- Protractor
- Ruler

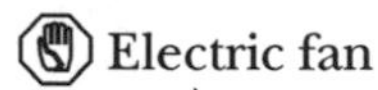

Electric fan

= **Safety icon**

HELPFUL HINTS AND DISCUSSION

Time frame: 40 minutes, or a single period of instruction

Structure: Individuals, or groups of two students

Location: In class

In this activity, students will study the wedge as it applies to a windmill. Make sure you define the wedge for them and that they understand the blade of a windmill as a wedge. Students will construct their own windmills. If they do the activity individually, they should be provided with materials to make two windmills so that they can directly compare the results for two blade angles. For safety reasons, the pencils provided should not have points. Use new, unsharpened pencils or neatly saw the points off used pencils. They should have most of the eraser intact. The thin cardboard should be stiffer than heavy paper, but not too thick or hard to cut with scissors.

Some students may need assistance regarding the angle of the blades. "High-angle" or "low-angle" are used to describe the angle between the direction of the wind and the blade. A high-angle blade is nearly perpendicular to the wind. The way the windmill is held, the disk from which the blades are cut and bent is also perpendicular to the wind. So, to make the low-angle blades, we must only bend the blade up from the disk a small amount (the "bend angle" is low).

ADAPTATIONS FOR HIGH AND LOW ACHIEVERS

High Achievers: Have these students supervise the low achievers as they construct their windmills. They should do the Follow-up Activity.

Low Achievers: Have these students work under the supervision of the higher-achieving students in the construction of their windmills.

SCORING RUBRIC

Full credit should be given to students whose data appear reasonable and who answer the questions correctly and in complete sentences. Extra credit should be given to students who complete the Extension and the Follow-up Activity. The quiz can be scored from 1 to 2 correct.

INTERNET TIE-INS

- For more about wedges:
  http://www.uark.edu/depts/aeedhp/agscience/simpmach.htm

QUIZ

1. The blade of a windmill is what type of simple machine?
2. A windmill like the one you built in this activity works best when the angle between the wind and its blades is which of the following: 5 degrees, 45 degrees, or 90 degrees? Explain your answer.

Name ______________________________ Date ______________________

How Can You Harness the Power of Wind with a Simple Machine?

STUDENT ACTIVITY PAGE

 BEFORE YOU BEGIN

In this activity, you are going to build your own miniature windmill. The blades of a windmill are **wedges**, since they are **inclined planes** that move. Most wedges (like an axe) convert the force of your muscles into a greater force to perform a task. You put power into the wedge, and the wedge does work on another object. Normal wedges are most useful when the angle is very small, like a very sharp blade, and the **mechanical advantage** is high.

Rather than consuming power to do work, a windmill *creates* mechanical power from the motion of the wind. The wind exerts force on the blades, which in turn exert force on the rest of the windmill so that it turns around an axis. The windmill then can do other useful work such as pumping water for irrigation. For your windmill, the wind of a fan supplies the power to turn the blades. Unlike normal wedges, though, mechanical advantage is not the only consideration for the blades of a windmill. A blade at a high angle to the direction of the wind (near 90 degrees) has a very low mechanical advantage and so would not overcome the force of friction very well. A blade at a low angle (near 0 degrees) and nearly parallel to the wind direction has a high mechanical advantage. But it isn't pushed very fast. What works best to efficiently convert the force of the wind into rotation is a compromise, with a blade angle about midway between 0 and 90 degrees.

After you construct your windmill, you and your partner will experiment with two blade angles: high and low. You will try both of these angles in front of a fan and observe how well each windmill works.

 MATERIALS

For each student or group of students:

- Thin cardboard sheet
- Unsharpened pencil with eraser
- Glue stick
- Pushpin
- Scissors (safety icon)
- Marker
- Masking tape
- Protractor
- Ruler
- Electric fan (safety icon)

(continued)

Name ______________________ Date ______________

How Can You Harness the Power of Wind with a Simple Machine? *(continued)*

STUDENT ACTIVITY PAGE

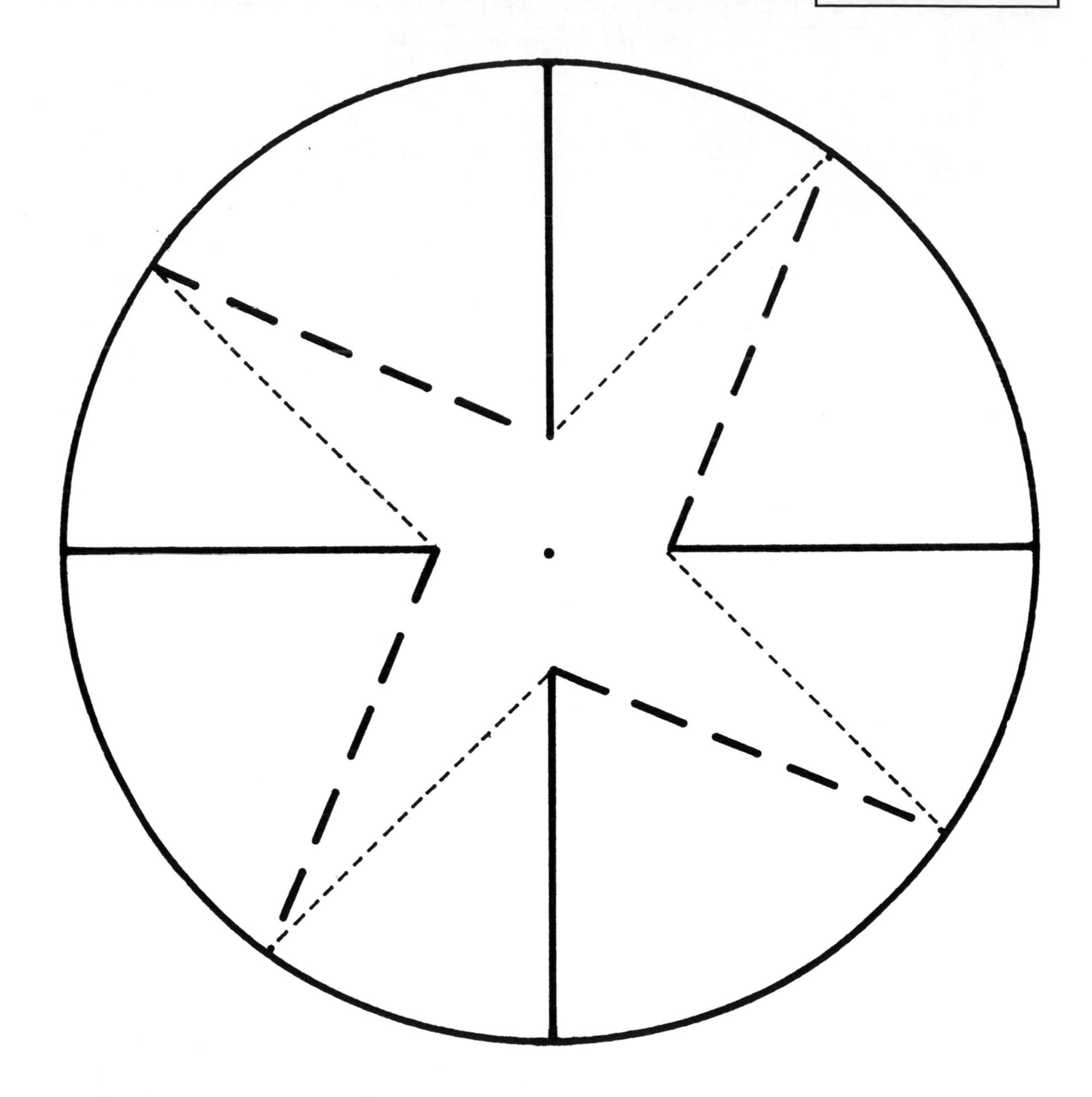

Figure 1

(continued)

Name ______________________ Date ______________

How Can You Harness the Power of Wind with a Simple Machine? *(continued)*

STUDENT ACTIVITY PAGE

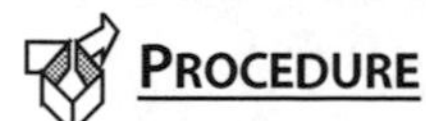

PROCEDURE

1. Using a photocopy of Figure 1, cover the area on the reverse side of the circle thoroughly with the glue stick. Glue the photocopy onto the thin cardboard sheet, printed side up. Using the scissors, *carefully* cut around the solid black circle to leave the disk. Discard the rest. Cut along each of the four straight, heavy solid lines from the edge toward the center, stopping where the solid lines end. Poke the pushpin through the black dot in the center. Wobble the pin around so it fits loosely and the disk can spin easily. Remove the pushpin.
2. With the disk lying flat on the desk or table in front of you, *carefully* fold the cardboard up along each of the thin dotted lines to make four raised segments, or blades. Using the protractor and viewing the disk from the edge, adjust the segments of your windmill so that each blade is raised to a bend angle of about 10 degrees from the table, which is a blade angle of 80 degrees from the wind. This is the high-angle windmill. Have your partner do the same with his or her windmill, but set the blades to about 45 degrees above the table, which is also 45 degrees from the wind. This is the low-angle windmill. Finally, cut along the heavy dashed lines to remove the pie-shaped pieces of cardboard between the blades.

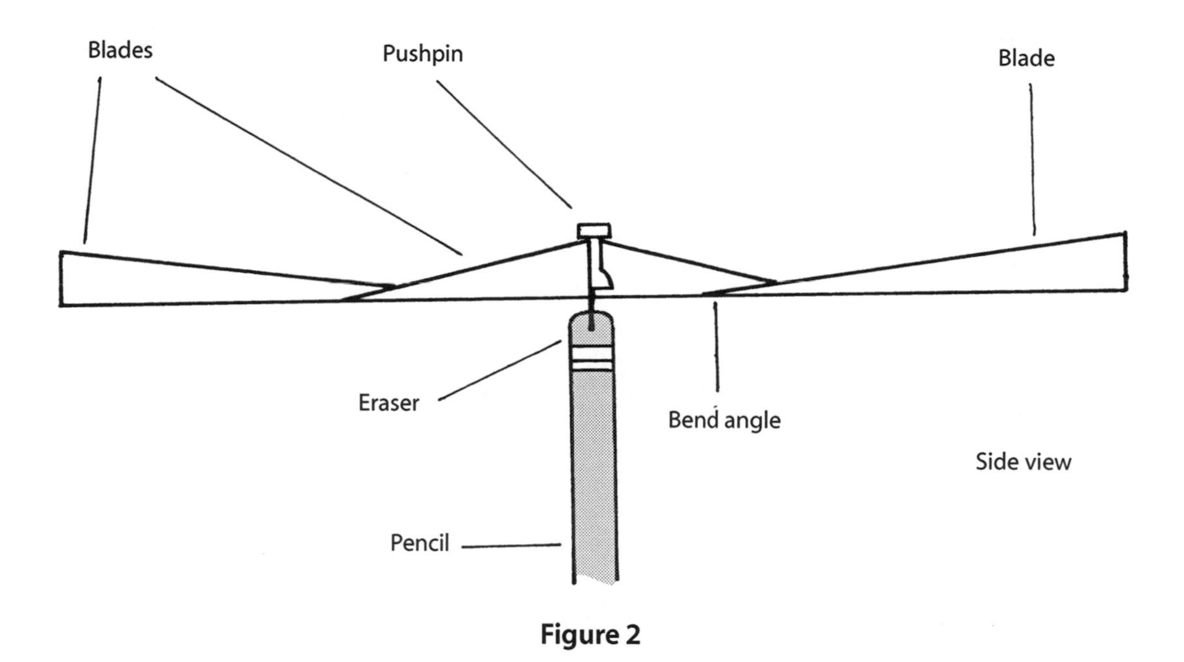

Figure 2

3. Put the point of the pushpin through the hole in the center of the disk from the printed side and then into the eraser of the pencil, as shown in Figure 2. Be sure the disk can spin freely. Back the pushpin out a bit if necessary so the disk is free to turn. The raised blades should be on the side away from the pencil.

(continued)

Name ______________________________ Date ____________________

How Can You Harness the Power of Wind with a Simple Machine? *(continued)*

STUDENT ACTIVITY PAGE

4. Place the fan on the floor. Measure 1 foot from the front of the fan and place a strip of masking tape on the floor at this location. Turn the fan on at its lowest setting.

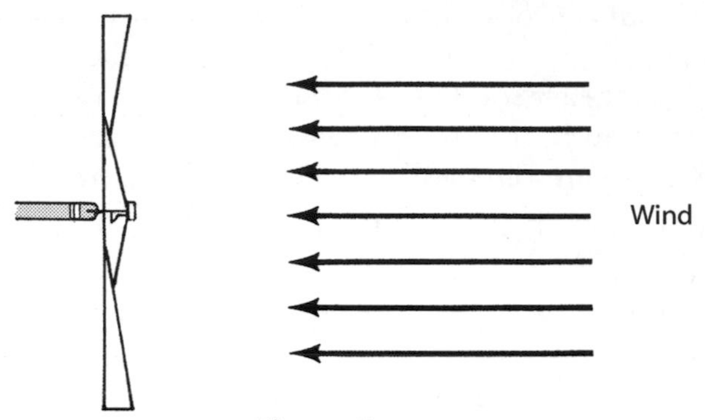

Figure 3

5. Using the tape for reference, both you and your partner should hold your windmills 1 foot in front of the fan, in the strongest part of the breeze (Figure 3). Observe which windmill spins faster—the one with blades at a high angle to the wind or the one with low-angle blades. You may wish to put a small dot on each windmill with the marker to better observe the rotation. Confirm your result by swapping windmills (put the 80-degree windmill where the 45-degree one was, and vice versa) and observing again. In the Data Collection and Analysis section, record your subjective impression of which spins faster and which spins slower.

EXTENSION: Set the blades of the low-angle windmill to an angle of 90 degrees from the table, or 0 degrees to the wind. Repeat step 5, comparing the 45-degree windmill to the one with blades parallel to the wind.

DATA COLLECTION AND ANALYSIS

Angle of Blade	Speed of Windmill (Faster or Slower)
10 degrees	
45 degrees	

EXTENSION

Angle of Blade	Speed of Windmill (Faster or Slower)
10 degrees	
90 degrees	

(continued)

Name ______________________________ Date ______________

How Can You Harness the Power of Wind with a Simple Machine? *(continued)*

STUDENT ACTIVITY PAGE

CONCLUDING QUESTIONS

1. On the basis of your observations in step 5, what is the relationship between the angle of the blade and the speed of the windmill? Why is this so?______________________________

____

____

____

2. Your windmill actually consists of two machines. What is the other one? ______________

____

____

____

EXTENSION: Does decreasing the angle between the blade and the wind always make a windmill work better? Why or why not? ______________________________

____

____

____

Follow-up Activity

Research and write a report on windmills and their significance throughout history. What purposes have they served? What cultures have made use of them? What importance might they hold for the future as we search for alternative energy sources in the 21st century? Build a replica of an old-fashioned windmill. Have it perform a useful function.

How Do Pulleys Work Together to Make a Better Machine?

TEACHER RESOURCE PAGE

INSTRUCTIONAL OBJECTIVES

Students will be able to

- understand how a pulley system makes a task easier.
- predict the mechanical advantage of a pulley system.
- calculate the work input and the work output of a pulley system.

NATIONAL SCIENCE STANDARDS ADDRESSED

Students produce evidence that demonstrates understanding of

- motions and forces.

Students demonstrate skill in scientific inquiry by

- working in teams to collect and share information and ideas.

Students demonstrate competence with the tools of science by

- using tools to observe and measure with appropriate consideration of accuracy.

MATERIALS

For each group of students:

- Four pulleys
- Clothesline or other strong cord
- Spring scale with attached hook
- Two meter sticks
- Load weight with hook

HELPFUL HINTS AND DISCUSSION

Time frame: 50 minutes, or a single period of instruction
Structure: Cooperative learning groups
Location: In class

In this activity, students will investigate the change in mechanical advantage that occurs when they add more pulleys to a system. They will discover that the mechanical advantage is roughly equal to the number of supporting ropes. In addition, students will see that an increase in mechanical advantage, such as that provided by additional pulleys, requires that the load be lifted through a longer effort distance. They will also calculate the work performed by the various pulley systems and should find that work input is slightly greater than work output due to the effects of friction.

You should obtain weights, spring scales, and cord or rope appropriate for whatever size pulleys you have available. The range of the spring scale should be great enough to measure the force of raising the weight with the single fixed pulley (mechanical advantage of 1), but not much greater. For example, with small clothesline pulleys about 2 inches in diameter you could use a 1.5-kilogram weight and a spring scale reading up to 20 newtons (1.5 kilograms corresponds to about 15 newtons). Devise a means of supporting the upper pulley(s) at an appropriate height above the floor, depending on the physical facilities and materials available at your institution.

Be sure to try this activity with the materials available before assigning it to the class. You may need to experiment with the attachment point between the spring scale and the cord to allow sufficient travel to lift the load the required distance. Demonstrate the way in which each arrangement is to be set up.

This activity may be a bit long for a single period of instruction. If the class has already done "How Does a Pulley Work?" you may want to skip Arrangement 1. If not, Arrangement 3 may be considered optional.

Adaptations for High and Low Achievers

High Achievers: Have these students perform the setup. These students should assist the lower-achieving students in collecting the data accurately during the activity. They should also be encouraged to do the Follow-up Activity.

Low Achievers: Have these students observe and record the measurements during the activity to gain more experience using scientific tools.

Scoring Rubric

Full credit should be given to students whose data appear reasonable and who answer the questions correctly and in complete sentences. Extra credit should be given to students who complete the Follow-up Activity. The quiz can be scored from 1 to 3 correct.

Internet Tie-Ins

- For more on pulleys:
  http://www.howstuffworks.com/pulley.htm
  http://infoplease.lycos.com/ce6/A0840500.html

Quiz

1. Which machine lets you perform a task with less force: one with a low mechanical advantage, or one with a high mechanical advantage?
2. What is the mechanical advantage of a pulley system with five cords supporting the movable pulleys?
3. Why must you actually do *more* work using a pulley system to lift a load than if you lift it directly?

Name ______________________ Date ______________

How Do Pulleys Work Together to Make a Better Machine?

STUDENT ACTIVITY PAGE

BEFORE YOU BEGIN

In this activity, you will discover how pulleys and pulley systems change the direction or the amount of force you apply. You will investigate how you can increase the **mechanical advantage** of the pulley in lifting a load by adding more pulleys. Mechanical advantage is the amount by which the applied force is multiplied by a machine. The higher the mechanical advantage, the less force is necessary to accomplish the same task. However, as the force decreases, the distance required to do the same work increases. You will discover that the mechanical advantage of each pulley system is roughly equal to the number of cords supporting the load.

One fixed pulley—a pulley that does not move with the load—does not by itself let you use less force. There is one cord supporting the load, so it has a mechanical advantage of 1. However, you can put pulleys together in such a way that you need to use much less force than the weight of the load. When working with pulleys, you calculate the mechanical advantage as usual. Divide the **effort distance** (the distance you pull the cord) by the **resistance distance** (the distance the load moves). You will also analyze the work you perform while using the pulleys and the work done by the pulleys on the load. *Work* is defined as force multiplied by the distance over which the force is applied. You will find that the force of friction that is present when using a machine actually makes you do more work, even though you can use less force.

MATERIALS

For each group of students:

- Four pulleys
- Clothesline or other strong cord
- Spring scale with attached hook
- Two meter sticks
- Load weight with hook

PROCEDURE

1. Using the spring scale, find the weight in newtons of the load provided by your teacher. Remember that this is the force required to lift the weight directly, without the help of a machine. Record this weight in the Data Collection and Analysis section (3 places).

(continued)

Name ______________________ Date ______________________

How Do Pulleys Work Together to Make a Better Machine? *(continued)*

STUDENT ACTIVITY PAGE.

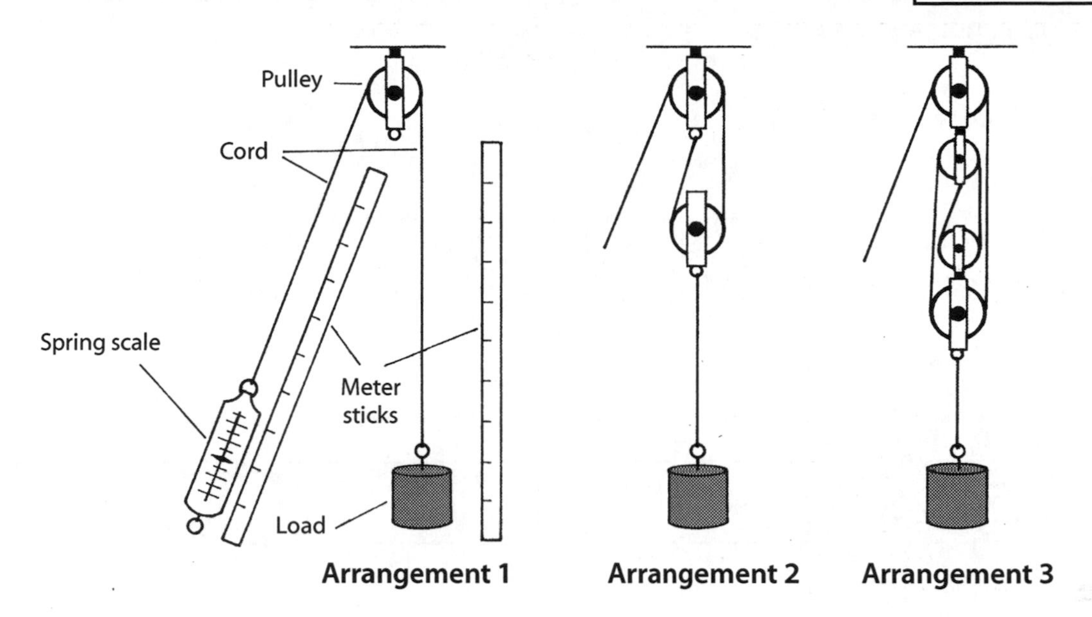

Figure 1

2. Set up Arrangement 1 as shown in Figure 1, with the load initially on a table or on the floor. Make sure a loop is tied in the cord to attach the hook on the spring scale. Arrange one meter stick next to the weight to measure the distance the load is lifted. Arrange the other meter stick in line with the cord to measure how far you pull the cord to lift the load. Check with your teacher to see if you have set this up correctly.
3. Pull on the spring scale to lift the load. Pull it slowly and smoothly, and stop when the load has moved 0.1 meters. Read the force on the scale as the load is moving and record it in the Data Collection and Analysis section.
4. After you stop pulling, measure and record how far the cord was pulled (in meters).
5. Count the number of supporting cords (cords which support *movable* pulleys attached to the load, plus 1 if there is a cord attached directly to the load). Record the number in the Data Collection and Analysis section.
6. Do steps 2 through 5 twice more, for arrangements 2 and 3. Record the data.
7. Calculate the mechanical advantage for each arrangement. Divide the distance you pulled the cord (effort distance) by the distance the load moved (resistance distance). Record these values in the Data Collection and Analysis section.
8. Calculate the work input for each arrangement. Multiply the force measured on the scale (effort force, in newtons) by the distance in meters that you moved the scale to lift the load. Calculate the work output by multiplying the weight of the load (resistance force) by the vertical distance that the load travels.

(continued)

Name ______________________________ Date ______________

How Do Pulleys Work Together to Make a Better Machine? *(continued)*

STUDENT ACTIVITY PAGE.

DATA COLLECTION AND ANALYSIS

Measured weight of load _______ newtons

	Arrangement 1	Arrangement 2	Arrangement 3
Force Needed to Lift Load (newtons)			
Distance the Cord Is Pulled (meters)			
Distance the Load Travels (meters)	0.1	0.1	0.1
# of Supporting Cords			
Mechanical Advantage			
Work Input (newton-meters)			
Work Output (newton-meters)			

CONCLUDING QUESTIONS

1. From your measurements and observations, what is the approximate relationship between the mechanical advantage of a pulley system and the number of cords supporting movable pulleys?

____

____

____

2. Explain why your answer to question 1 is not exact. What other force is present when you use a machine that is not significant when you lift a load directly? ______________________________

____

____

____

(continued)

Name ______________________________ Date ____________________

How Do Pulleys Work Together to Make a Better Machine? *(continued)*

STUDENT ACTIVITY PAGE

3. Does doubling the mechanical advantage of a pulley system reduce the work you must do to lift a load a certain distance by half? Explain why the work put into the system is different from the work put out by the system. ______________________________
____
____
____

Follow-up Activity

Pulley systems are not as common today as they were at some times in the past. They were, for example, used heavily on the seagoing sailing ships of previous centuries. They also were once important tools in building construction and maintenance and in cargo handling. Investigate and write a brief report on the ways in which pulleys were used. Find some models of old ships or photographs that illustrate such uses. Be sure to find and include information on the particular configuration called a *block and tackle.* For each use that you describe, explain why pulleys have been replaced by other types of machines, or why the job once done by pulley systems has disappeared entirely.

How Do Gears Work?

TEACHER RESOURCE PAGE

INSTRUCTIONAL OBJECTIVES

Students will be able to

- describe the function of gears as simple machines.
- demonstrate the properties of a gear set.

NATIONAL SCIENCE STANDARDS ADDRESSED

Students produce evidence that demonstrates understanding of

- motions and forces.

Students demonstrate scientific inquiry and problem-solving skills by

- working individually and in teams to collect and share information and ideas.
- using concepts to explain observed phenomena.

Students demonstrate effective scientific communication by

- arguing from evidence and data.

MATERIALS

For each group of students:

- Thin ($\frac{1}{8}$" to $\frac{3}{16}$") foam board
- Three pushpins
- Glue stick
- Marker
- Thin plywood, wall paneling, or foam board, about 30–40 cm square

Scissors

= Safety icon

HELPFUL HINTS AND DISCUSSION

Time frame: 50 minutes, or one period of instruction
Structure: Groups of 2 or 3 students
Location: In class

Make at least three copies of Figure 2 for each group of students. Each copy will be used as a pattern to make a gear. Show the students examples of properly constructed gears.

The thin foam board specified can be found at stationery or art supply stores and is often used for mounting photographs or poster presentations. Provide each student with enough foam board to cut out all three gears. Help the students place the templates on the foam board so that they get all three gears from the material provided. Other materials may be substituted, but may not work as well. Use good-quality, full-sized scissors—the foam board may be hard to cut. Similarly, corrugated cardboard may be used in place of the thin plywood, wall paneling, or foam board specified as the baseboard of the assembled gear set, but it does not hold the pushpins in place as well. The students may need help placing the gears on the baseboard so that the gears rotate freely.

ADAPTATIONS FOR HIGH AND LOW ACHIEVERS

High Achievers: These students should be encouraged to do the Extension and the Follow-up Activity.

Low Achievers: Review the idea that the circumference of a circle (and thus the number of teeth that can fit around a gear) is proportional to the diameter of the circle. These students can be paired with high achievers for the activity.

Scoring Rubric

Full credit should be given to students who correctly build the gears, place them on the board as a gear set, and observe the correct numbers of teeth and turns, and who answer the questions correctly and in complete sentences. Extra credit should be awarded to students who do the Extension or Follow-up Activity. The quiz can be scored from 1 to 4 correct.

Internet Tie-ins

- For more on gears, see:

  http://srl.marc.gatech.edu/education/ME3110/primer/geartit.htm
  http://www.cpo.com/CPOCatalog/GL/gl_sci.htm

Quiz

1. A gear is a type of what basic simple machine?
2. A gear with 30 teeth rotates at 1 turn per second. If it drives a second gear with 60 teeth, how fast will the second gear rotate?
3. In question 2 above, how much force can the second gear exert compared to the force turning the first gear?
4. True or false: Every pair of spur gears reverses the direction of rotation.

Name ______________________ Date ______________

How Do Gears Work?

STUDENT ACTIVITY PAGE

BEFORE YOU BEGIN

If you look inside a mechanical clock or an automobile transmission, you will see a variety of circular objects with bumps, or "teeth," around their edges. These are called **gears**. They are a special kind of wheel. Like other **machines**, gears are used to change the speed or direction of motion or to change the force applied to an object. A single gear is never used alone. There must be at least one other gear for its teeth to mesh with, as shown in Figure 1. The teeth in both gears must be the same size.

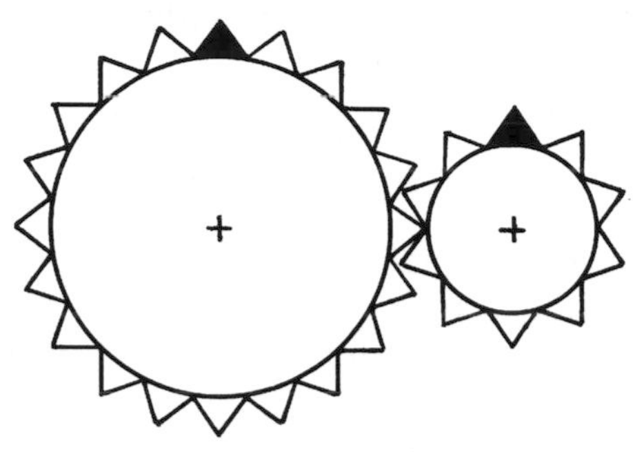

Figure 1

The amount by which a gear set changes the motion depends on the relative number of teeth on the gears, which in turn depends on the diameters of the gears. If you rotate a gear with 100 teeth, another gear with 50 teeth meshed with the first will rotate twice as fast as the one you are turning, but it requires that you exert twice the force. It will also rotate in the opposite direction! There are many kinds of gears. The particular type of gear shown here is called a "spur" gear because it resembles the spur on a cowboy's boot. Any pair of spur gears working together must lie in the same plane, and each rotates around its own axis. On real, practical gears the teeth are a special shape—not the simple triangles used here.

MATERIALS

For each group of students:

- Thin ($\frac{1}{8}$" to $\frac{3}{16}$") foam board
- Three pushpins
- Glue stick
- Marker
- Thin plywood, wall paneling, or foam board, about 30–40 cm square

Scissors

= Safety icon

(continued)

Name ______________________ Date ______________________

How Do Gears Work? *(continued)*

STUDENT ACTIVITY PAGE

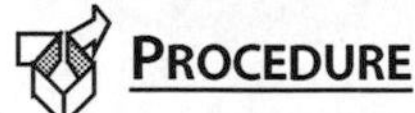

PROCEDURE

Your teacher will provide you with three copies of Figure 2, which contains templates (line drawings) of three different-sized gears, one inside another.

1. Using the glue stick, glue a copy of Figure 2 (printed side up) onto the foam board toward one corner. Using the scissors, *carefully* cut out the largest gear. Cut through both the foam board and the template, and follow the lines as closely as you can. This is gear "A."
2. Repeat step 1, using the middle gear template from Figure 2. This is gear "B."
3. Repeat step 1, using the smallest gear template from Figure 2. This is gear "C."
4. Push a pin through the center of each of the gears, being careful to keep the shaft of the pin perpendicular to the surface of the gear. Wobble the pin around a bit to loosen the fit so the disk can spin easily.
5. Pin gear A to the plywood baseboard. Make sure that the pushpin is well attached and that the gear is free to rotate. Do the same for gear C, placing it on the board so that its teeth are meshed with those of gear A, as shown in Figure 1. Make a mark on the baseboard at the tip of the black triangle of gear A, and do the same for gear C.
6. Have one student observe gear A and another observe gear C. Have one of you, or a third student, rotate gear C *clockwise* until gear A has gone one full rotation. Estimate (to the nearest whole turn) the number of turns of gear C that were needed to make one rotation of gear A. Record your result in the Data Collection and Analysis section. Also note the direction of rotation of gear A and circle either "clockwise" or "counterclockwise" in the Data Collection and Analysis section.
7. Repeat steps 5 and 6 using gears A and B. Rotate gear B until gear A has gone three full turns, and estimate the number of turns of gear B that were needed to make 3 rotations of gear A.
8. Count the number of "teeth" on each of the three gears, and record your results in the Data Collection and Analysis section.

EXTENSION: In step 6 we can think of gear C as the "input" and gear A as the "output." Construct a gear set in which the output gear rotates once for every two rotations of the input gear, but *in the same direction.*

(continued)

Name ______________________ Date ______________________

How Do Gears Work? *(continued)*

STUDENT ACTIVITY PAGE

Figure 2

(continued)

Name ______________________________ Date ________________

How Do Gears Work? *(continued)*

STUDENT ACTIVITY PAGE

DATA COLLECTION AND ANALYSIS

of turns of C for 1 turn of A _______ (turns: clockwise/counterclockwise)

# of turns of B for 3 turns of A _______ (turns: clockwise/counterclockwise)

# of teeth on gear A _______

# of teeth on gear B _______

# of teeth on gear C _______

CONCLUDING QUESTIONS

1. Why are gears considered simple machines?______________________________
____
____

2. What is the ratio of the number of teeth on gear A to the number of teeth on gear C? How many turns did gear C make for one turn of gear A in step 6? Explain why this is so.______________
____
____
____

3 How did these numbers change when you used gears A and B in step 7? Why? ______________
____
____
____

4. What happens to the direction of rotation when you use one spur gear to rotate another? _____
____
____
____
____

(continued)

Name ______________________________ Date ________________

How Do Gears Work? *(continued)*

STUDENT ACTIVITY PAGE

EXTENSION: Sets of three or more gears can be analyzed by considering in turn each meshed pair (gears A & B, B & C, etc.). In a gear set of the type shown here, does the number of rotations of the output gear for each rotation of the input gear depend on the number of teeth on the gears in between them? What determines the direction of rotation of the output gear? Explain your answers.____

____

____

____

____

____

Follow-up Activity

Most bicycles have gears and a chain to transmit power from you to the wheels. Unlike the gears in this activity, a chain is used to connect these gears. But the principle is the same. Obtain a bicycle. Now shift speeds so that the chain is on the largest gear of the front group and the smallest gear of the back group. Count and record the number of teeth on each of these gears. Verify by experiment that the number of turns of the rear wheel for every turn of the pedals is equal to the number of teeth on the front gear divided by the number of teeth on the back gear. **Be very careful to avoid getting fingers, hair or clothing caught in the gears and spokes of the biycle.**

How Are Simple Machines Classified?

TEACHER RESOURCE PAGE

INSTRUCTIONAL OBJECTIVES

Students will be able to

- identify and classify simple machines.

NATIONAL SCIENCE STANDARDS ADDRESSED

Students produce evidence that demonstrates understanding of

- motions and forces.

Students demonstrate skill in scientific inquiry by

- working individually and in teams to collect and share information.

MATERIALS

For each group of students:

- Variety of broken machines
- Variety of small tools, including screwdrivers, wrenches, Allen wrenches, and pliers
- Protective eyewear (for *every* student)
- Six copies of Data Collectiona nd Analysis Chart
- Pen, pencil, or marker
- Ruler

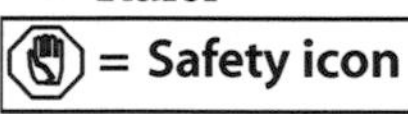

HELPFUL HINTS AND DISCUSSION

Time frame: 50 minutes, or a single period of instruction
Structure: Cooperative learning groups
Location: In class

In this activity, students will be bringing to class all sorts of broken machines from their homes and neighborhoods. Be sure to leave some time for students to collect a sufficient supply. Guide the students to bring in machines that are mechanical or have moving parts and to get clear permission from their parents to destroy these items (you may wish to require a signed note to that effect). Good examples are a mechanical clock, a portable stereo, a hand mixer, and many kinds of toys, such as a radio-controlled car. You may also be able to obtain some discarded devices around the school and from local hardware, appliance, or toy retailers and repair shops. Most electronic devices will not provide enough simple machines for this activity. Break the class up into as many learning groups as you have good devices for. Some groups may need to disassemble more than one device to get enough parts. Some of the tools may be in short supply, so encourage the groups to share them.

Remind students of the six basic simple machines: lever, inclined plane, wedge, screw, pulley, and wheel. They must be able to recognize variations of these machines as well. For example, a gear is a wheel and axle, and a switch may be a lever. Allocate about half the class time for disassembly, and half for identification.

Safety Issues: Make sure you check the machines for potential safety hazards such as sharp points or edges. Do not allow any student to proceed if you suspect there is risk of injury and cannot remove the source. If the device is electrically powered, do not under any circumstances plug the device in. If the device contains batteries, remove and dispose of them properly. Warn the students that taking apart machines can have unpredictable results, such as pieces flying off. Make certain that all students are provided with and wear appropriate protective eyewear during the entire disassembly time, even if they have finished with their own devices. Students will probably enjoy this aspect of the activity, but be careful to not let things get out of control. This activity should be fun, not dangerous.

ADAPTATIONS FOR HIGH AND LOW ACHIEVERS

High Achievers: Have these students assist the low achievers as they attempt to identify the various pieces of the machines. They should also be encouraged to do the Follow-up Activities.

Low Achievers: Review with these students the six simple machines and the various forms they can come in. Review the functions of each so they can recognize a machine by its function.

SCORING RUBRIC

Full credit should be given to students whose classifications are correct. Extra credit should be given to students who complete the Follow-up Activities. The quiz can be scored from 1 to 2 correct.

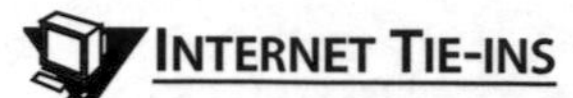

INTERNET TIE-INS

- For more on classifying simple machines:
  http://www.science-tech.nmstc.ca/engine.cfm?function=link&idx=1394&language=english#simple

QUIZ

1. What are the six basic simple machines?
2. What simple machines are found in a manual staple remover?

Name ______________________________ Date ______________

How Are Simple Machines Classified?

STUDENT ACTIVITY SHEET

 **BEFORE YOU BEGIN** 

Our world is full of machines, gadgets, and toys that are composed, at least in part, of many simple machines. These simple machines together do work that, helps the overall device function as intended. For example, even a simple manual staple remover includes a lever and several wedges. In this activity, you will be taking apart broken devices that you have scrounged from your home, school, or neighborhood. Be careful when you take them apart because they were probably not designed to be disassembled. You may encounter some unpredictable breaks in the material and pieces may fly out. **Be sure to wear the protective eyewear that your teacher provides**. Once you have fully disassembled your machine, identify all the pieces you think function as simple machines within the larger, complex machine. You will organize and put these pieces (the simple machines) into the six categories of simple machines: the lever, the inclined plane, the wedge, the screw, the pulley, and the wheel.

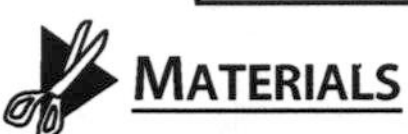

MATERIALS

For each group of students:

- Variety of broken machines
- Variety of small tools, including screwdrivers, wrenches, Allen wrenches, and pliers
- Protective eyewear (for *every* student)
- Six copies of Data Collection and Analysis Chart
- Pen, pencil, or marker
- Ruler

PROCEDURE

1. Choose the machine or machines you will disassemble.
2. Before proceeding, **put on the protective eyewear** provided by your teacher. Do not take it off until all teams have completed disassembly.
3. Working as a team, take the machine apart as fully as you can. Try to do so without breaking plastic parts, but if you do need to break things, be careful to avoid hurting yourself or others. Do not stop until no two pieces are connected to each other.
4. Identify those pieces that look like simple machines. Before you discard those that are not, check with your teacher to see if you may have missed any machines.

(continued)

Name ______________________ Date ______________

How Are Simple Machines Classified? *(continued)*

STUDENT ACTIVITY SHEET

5. On each of the copies of the Data Collection and Analysis Chart from the Data Collection and Analysis section enter one of the following six categories as the heading:

   Lever Inclined Plane Wedge Screw Pulley Wheel

6. Use your copies of the Data Collection and Analysis Chart to register all your simple machine pieces in their proper categories. Do this by describing the part (such as "½-inch-long bolt") on the sheet with the heading corresponding to the proper type of simple machine. Use the ruler to help in your description of the parts. If you cannot name or recognize a piece, you may draw it. Or you may describe what you think may be its function in the complex machine. Make and use additional copies of the table if needed.
7. When you have identified and categorized all your pieces, for each category count the number of simple machines of that type that you found, and write the number in the lower right-hand corner.
8. Clean up!

CONCLUDING QUESTIONS

1. What is the most frequently occurring simple machine (lever, ramp, etc.) in the complex machine or machines that you took apart? What is this simple machine mainly used for? Why do you think this is so? ______________________

   ____

   ____

   ____

2. Which simple machine occurred least frequently, or perhaps not at all? Can you think of a machine in which this type of simple machine does appear? ______________________

   ____

   ____

   ____

Follow-up Activities

1. Reassemble some of the simple machines from this activity to make a complex machine of your own devising.
2. Make a Rube Goldberg drawing. A Rube Goldberg drawing is a diagram in which a complicated combination of various machines and devices operates in a chain reaction to ultimately perform a very simple function.

(continued)

Name ______________________________ Date ____________________

How Are Simple Machines Classified? *(continued)*

STUDENT ACTIVITY SHEET

DATA COLLECTION AND ANALYSIS

Category ____________________
Number of machines found: _____

Simple Machines Everywhere

TEACHER RESOURCE PAGE

INSTRUCTIONAL OBJECTIVES

Students will be able to

- appreciate the diverse application of simple machines.
- demonstrate their understanding of simple machines in creative ways.

NATIONAL SCIENCE STANDARDS ADDRESSED

Students produce evidence that demonstrates understanding of

- the impact of science, such as historical and contemporary contributions.
- interactions between science and society.

Students demonstrate scientific inquiry and problem solving skills by

- using evidence from reliable sources.
- working in teams to collect and share information and ideas.

Students demonstrate effective scientific communication by

- arguing from evidence and data.

MATERIALS

For each group of students:

- Internet access
- Reference books
- Museum access

HELPFUL HINTS AND DISCUSSION

Time frame: 50 minutes, or one period of instruction, for presentations

Structure: Three self-selected groups of students

Location: In class, at home, and elsewhere as needed

This group research activity is an opportunity for the students to go beyond the straightforward description and applications of simple machines and to consider the impact of these ideas in a broader context. Three topics are offered for research and reports, but you may wish to add an interesting topic of your own. Students should be encouraged to gather data from a variety of *reliable* sources, including reference and text books, encyclopedias, and (with some care) the Internet. Web sites composed by museums, libraries, businesses, and educational institutions of all types are usually reliable, but individuals' sites, including those of other students, generally should not be used. For the topic "Simple Machines in Nature" a good reference might be an anatomy book or a general biology text. Help the students look for relevant museum exhibits. Have the students list all their sources.

Through your technology coordinator or similar staff, try to make web space available so that a group may create its own web pages as one means of reporting on what was learned. This should be easy, since web browser software usually includes a simple editor for composing web pages. Some students of this age are amazingly quick at picking up the needed skills, or they may already have done so.

You may wish to set up one research group for each topic, allowing students to self-select into these groups. Give the groups two or three weeks to do the research and create their presentations, which should then be given during classroom time. Possibilities include demonstration of their web pages, demonstration of an example or model of a machine, or a dramatic presentation. Encourage the students to be creative—try to avoid having students simply read reports aloud in class.

Students may require some help in thinking about Topic B—Simple Machines in Nature. For example (you could say), your front teeth are pretty clearly wedges, and your arm includes several levers. Urge them to think about the functions performed by parts of plants and animals, and what makes those parts function better. In weather, a cold front acts as a wedge pushing underneath a warm air mass.

ADAPTATIONS FOR HIGH AND LOW ACHIEVERS

High Achievers: No adaptations are necessary.

Low Achievers: Review the six basic types of simple machines.

Scoring Rubric

Due to the unique nature of this activity, we suggest that each of the groups be given a collective, advisory grade (not counted toward a student's final grade). This grade may be based on your evaluation of the quality of the group's collaborative research and their creativity in presenting what they have learned. Extra credit (which *may* count toward a student's final grade) should be awarded to students who do the Follow-up Activity. The quiz can be scored from 1 to 2 correct.

Internet Tie-ins

- For more background on simple machines:
  http://www.robinsonresearch.com/TECHNOL/the_basics.htm
  http://www.science-tech.nmstc.ca/engine.cfm?function=link&idx=1394&language=english#simple

Quiz

1. Explain how simple machines are important to the industrialized world.
2. Name three reliable sources of information for this research activity. What kinds of web sites should not be considered good sources of accurate information?

Name ______________________ Date ______________

Simple Machines Everywhere

STUDENT ACTIVITY PAGE

 **BEFORE YOU BEGIN** 

By now you have seen several examples of each kind of simple machine. You have also seen several compound machines consisting of at least two, and often many, simple machines working together. Perhaps you have developed an appreciation for the widespread usefulness of simple machines in our world. In this activity you will research one of three topics related to simple machines. This group research activity is a chance to go beyond the ideas discussed in the other activities and to consider their impact more broadly. Reliable sources for your research include encyclopedias, text and reference books, and (with some care) the Internet. Web sites composed by museums, libraries, businesses, and educational institutions of all types are usually reliable. Individuals' web sites, however, including those of other students, generally should not be considered totally reliable. You may want to look for and visit relevant museum exhibits.

MATERIALS

For each group of students:

- Internet access
- Library access
- Museum access

PROCEDURE

1. Three topics related to simple machines are described below. Your teacher may provide additional topics. The class will be divided into groups—one group to research and report on each topic. Select the group that you wish to work in.
2. As a group, organize yourselves to gather data from all available *reliable* sources. Be sure to keep a list of all your sources.
3. As a group, present your results to the class in a creative way. Possibilities include composing the information into web pages, demonstrating an example or model of a machine, or giving a dramatic presentation. Use your imagination! Plan for your presentation to take about one fourth of a class period.

SUGGESTED TOPICS

A. 17th- through 19th-Century Mechanical Devices

Mechanical toys and amusements have been around since ancient times. But the development of such machines in the form of clocks, music boxes, and automatons (mechanical simulations of living beings) flourished during the 17th, 18th, and 19th centuries. Research these devices. Find out why and how they were made, what simple machines were incorporated into their construction, and what functions those simple machines performed. How are these early mechanical devices related to the modern science of robotics?

(continued)

Name ____________________ Date ____________

Simple Machines Everywhere

STUDENT ACTIVITY PAGE

B. Simple Machines in Nature

We usually think of machines as products of human engineering. The making and use of tools, including machines, is often cited as one characteristic that is almost uniquely human. There are, however, examples of simple machines in nature—machines that were not built by people. Some of these are found in the structure of living beings—plants and animals. A few may be tools of a kind, but tools used not by humans but by other animals. At least one is found in the behavior of weather! Research these natural machines. List as many of these as you can (a minimum of five) and describe how they work. What types of simple machines are *never* found in nature?

C. The Automobile

The automobile is one of the most common machines. It symbolizes to many our industrial world. Research the invention of the automobile and how it has developed over the years into a very complex and sophisticated machine. Find out what a few of the many simple machines incorporated into an automobile do to help make the machine as a whole function better. In addition to the usual research resources, it may be helpful to spend a little time going over an automobile to find some of the less obvious places where simple machines are used. Which type of simple machine occurs the most frequently in a typical automobile?

Concluding Questions

1. What is the most interesting single piece of information you learned about simple machines while doing your research?
2. How did you feel about working in a group? What problems did you encounter getting the work done?

Follow-up Activity

In this activity you were encouraged to report your findings as a group, and in a creative manner. As an individual, choose an aspect of the topic your group researched and explore it more deeply. For example, if your group worked on "17th- through 19th-Century Mechanical Devices," learn as much as you can about a particular artifact. Find out when it was made and by whom, how it was constructed, and what the simple machines in it were used for. Describe its historical importance, if any, or why it turned out to have no such significance. If your group worked on another topic, do a similar in-depth exploration within that topic. Present the results of your in-depth research in the form of a short written report.

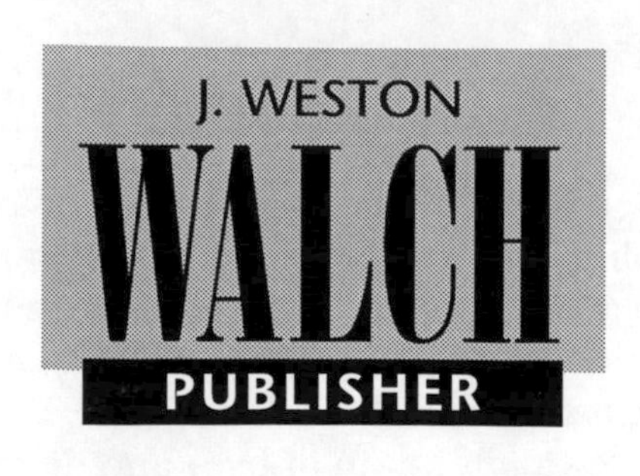

Share Your Bright Ideas with Us!

We want to hear from you! Your valuable comments and suggestions will help us meet your current and future classroom needs.

Your name____ Date____________________

School name_____________________________________ Phone_________________________

School address____

Grade level taught________ Subject area(s) taught____________________________ Average class size_____

Where did you purchase this publication?____

Was your salesperson knowledgeable about this product? Yes_____ No_____

What monies were used to purchase this product?

___School supplemental budget ___Federal/state funding ___Personal

Please "grade" this Walch publication according to the following criteria:

Quality of service you received when purchasing	A	B	C	D	F
Ease of use	A	B	C	D	F
Quality of content	A	B	C	D	F
Page layout	A	B	C	D	F
Organization of material	A	B	C	D	F
Suitability for grade level	A	B	C	D	F
Instructional value	A	B	C	D	F

COMMENTS:____

____

What specific supplemental materials would help you meet your current—or future—instructional needs?

____

Have you used other Walch publications? If so, which ones?_______________________________

May we use your comments in upcoming communications? ___Yes ___No

Please **FAX** this completed form to **207-772-3105**, or mail it to:

Product Development, J.Weston Walch, Publisher, P.O. Box 658, Portland, ME 04104-0658

We will send you a **FREE GIFT** as our way of thanking you for your feedback. **THANK YOU!**